THE River of Life

THE STORY OF MAN'S BLOOD FROM MAGIC TO SCIENCE

BERNARD
SEEMAN

MUSEUM PRESS LIMITED · *London*

FIRST PUBLISHED IN GREAT BRITAIN BY MUSEUM PRESS
LIMITED, 26 OLD BROMPTON ROAD, LONDON, S.W.7
1962

PRINTED IN GREAT BRITAIN BY
LOWE AND BRYDONE (PRINTERS) LTD., LONDON

R. 3469

Contents

Part Five: The River We Know

ILLUSTRATIONS

(Between pages 128 and 129)

Acknowledgments

No. 8 is reproduced by gracious permission of Her Majesty the Queen. No. 23, the photograph of the Melrose N.E.P. heart-lung machine, is reproduced by permission of the Postgraduate Medical School of London. Illustations nos. 1-7 and 9-20 are from the Radio Times Hulton Picture Library.

Author's Note

Our knowledge of the blood was long and hard in coming. Ignorance, superstition and dogma have cloaked the blood in mystery almost from the beginning. Among those who challenged ignorance to explore the river of life are many heroes and even a few martyrs. What they have given us is a map of the river, a description of much of its course and a glimpse into many of the events that take place along its route.

In addition, and in some ways almost as important as the knowledge they provided, they have made us better able to perceive the areas of darkness that still remain. By helping us define what we do not know, they have set our steps in the direction of knowing.

Prologue

The Hidden Spring

The earth was hot with the violence of its birth.

There was no life. There was not even the sea; and much of what is now the physical substance of earth was, in that unimaginable heat, gas and vapor. Then, as the earth slowly cooled, the vapors began to condense and fall back in great rains. Finally, the sea was formed.

Eons passed as streams, pouring over the rocks and gradually eroding them, flowed into the sea carrying salts, minerals and tiny particles of dust. In time, a sediment formed and was deposited on the shores and sea bottoms; and the waters themselves became charged with the chemicals they carried, either in solution or held in suspension. Still, there was no life.

For millions and millions of years, as we now suspect, the tides and currents of the sea brought together infinitely changing combinations of chemicals under differing conditions of heat, pressure, electrical charge and sunlight until appeared one with a property never possessed by any of the combinations that had come before. That property was life.

This first and most primitive capsule of living matter was a simple cell, undoubtedly formed of protoplasm, the basic stuff of life.

Since it arose from the sea, its fundamental content was of the sea. Protoplasm was—and still is—mainly water and a small amount of carbon, nitrogen, oxygen, hydrogen intricately combined to form what we know as protein. In addition, the cell probably contained some sulphur, phosphorus and various minerals that existed in the water around it. But, while the cell was much like the sea from which it evolved, there was one fundamental difference. Its combination of substances had come together to form a unique and self-sustaining balance.

Unlike the swirling, changing but lifeless sea, the cell had a set of qualities never before combined into any single entity. It had irritability—that is, it could react to internal or external change or other stimuli. It could grow. It could take necessary substances from the surrounding environment and convert them into heat, energy and other essential products. Finally, it could reproduce itself. With these four qualities, the cell entered into that mysterious and somewhat dimly-defined state that we call life.

The same combination of circumstances that formed the first cell may have occurred a number of times and, as some scientists believe, may take place even today in the ocean deeps or the sediment of tidal basins. But whether it was the first cell or a more recent one, protoplasm was the substance of its life; and the sea around it, which bathed and nourished it, was the medium of its life.

Held within the sea were the chemical salts, the nutrients and the oxygen that were essential to the continued life of the cell. As these substances came into contact with the cell, they were absorbed through the cell wall. Meanwhile, the wastes created by the life processes within the cell were passed into the sea which carried them off.

But this alone is not sufficient for life. The sea also maintained a range of temperatures within which life could continue to exist; and it preserved the essential chemical balances and provided the delicate interplay of pressures without which the cell would have been obliterated.

The cell grew and reproduced itself by dividing into two. The two cells separated, grew again, divided, separated and so continued possibly for millions of years, while the sea nourished and maintained the expanding population of single cells. At some point, possibly as the result of a mutation, a cell divided but the resulting cells did not separate. With this a higher form of life had evolved, a more complex organism consisting of two cells.

Other mutations followed as the eons passed, and living organisms became larger and more complex. In some of these the interior cells were completely surrounded by other cells. Thus cut off from the sea, the source of their nourishment and the carrier of their wastes, they perished.

But other mutations survived and, through eons of natural selection, were able to compromise between the need for growth and the need for each of their cells to have direct contact with the sea.

Primitive life forms developed, consisting of many cells. Some of these had canals which permitted the sea to flow through their interiors, bringing oxygen and nutrients to their deepest cells and carrying away the wastes that would otherwise have poisoned them. The sponge is a surviving example of such a primitive life form. It is sustained by the ebb and flow of the sea through its canals.

In one of those early ages, a still newer organism evolved, possibly out of a creature with a canal circulation. This new form closed itself around the sea. The sea no longer flowed through this creature, carrying sustenance to its cells. Instead, food and oxygen were removed from the sea outside, passed through certain openings or membranes into the fluids of a closed circulatory system and thence to each of the cells. The wastes, carried by the same fluids, were passed through outer openings or membranes into the sea outside. Thus the river of life was born.

The organism out of which man ultimately evolved, encompassed and enclosed a portion of the sea. The watery environment that was essential to life and which primitive life forms could not leave, became the blood—an internal environment which, being portable, allowed this higher organism a mobility that had previously been impossible. Many could even leave the watery environment and explore the possibility of living on dry land or in the air. But, wherever they went, they could never fully forsake the mother sea. They carried it with them in their blood.

The identity between the blood and the sea is no mere figure of speech but a biochemical fact. The blood consists of a virtually colorless fluid in which are suspended a vast number of cells, red and white, the red cells being so overwhelmingly numerous as to give the blood its red color. Since it evolved from sea water and must perform the same functions that sea water once performed, one would expect some similarity. Actually, there is more than a similarity.

Sea water today is almost identical with blood serum except that it has a higher concentration of inorganic salts. When the difference in salt concentration was measured some years ago by the eminent physiologist A. B. Macallum, he reached an interesting conclusion which, in essence, wiped out the difference. The composition of sea water, he found, has changed somewhat through the ages. The sea of that time long past when venturesome life forms first left the water to adapt to life on land, was much more similar to our blood serum, which is about 92 percent water. It is this early sea, then, that courses through us carrying the various materials that make up the blood—proteins, certain inorganic salts and nutritive materials, hormones, enzymes and antibodies, and waste materials such as urea and uric acid.

The river of life, as it pulses through our bodies, is the result of an evolutionary process that spans the more than three billion years since, according to Professors I. G. Oparin and J. D. Bernal, the first living cell probably appeared. It is the longest river in the world. As it surges from the heart through the corridors of our arteries, capillaries and veins and returns to the heart, it flows along a route stretching between 60,000 and 100,000 miles. The exact distance has never been measured.

But we have charted the course of the blood and learned many of its functions. Thanks to such recent scientific marvels as the electron microscope, we have even been able to watch events inside the capillaries, blood vessels so incredibly thin that about 50,000 of them laid side by side would barely measure an inch.

The human body is a complex structure with its organs, its tissues, its connective materials, its fluids, its endocrine, nervous and other systems, all functioning in that exquisitely integrated harmony which we call life. Yet most of these structures are organizations of the one basic substance of life, the simple cell formed of protoplasm.

The average human body consists of hundreds of trillions of these cells, each with its own needs and its own cycle of life and death. Each of these cells is also delicately integrated into the group of cells which comprise the tissue or organ of which it is a part. It thus serves this greater need at the same time it serves its own individual needs.

In order to survive and perform its functions both as an individual and as a member of a highly organized group, each single cell must be constantly provided with the substances of life which it requires, and it must be relieved of the substances of death which it accumulates. This is one of the fundamental responsibilities of the blood.

The river of life is a transportation system far more intricate than any devised by man. Thrust out by the pumping heart, with its speed stabilized by the pulsing, muscular arteries, the blood is guided by a complex series of valves to the network of microscopic capillaries which it enters in a precisely regulated flow.

In the capillaries, which are often so narrow that the red cells must squeeze through in single file, the blood unloads the vital substances needed by each of the body cells. These materials include oxygen, picked up by the blood during a passage through the lungs; nutrients such as amino acids, sugars, fats and other materials delivered through the digestive system; and other substances such as hormones produced by specialized tissues of the body.

Passing from the capillaries to the veins on its way back to the heart, the blood carries carbon dioxide and other byproducts of life functions it has picked up from the cells. These wastes tend to give the returning blood a bluish color, and some of them are carried to organs of the body such as the lungs and kidneys, where they are removed from the blood. Other wastes are carried to specialized centers where they are reprocessed and rebuilt into materials the body can use again.

This is the cycle of the river of life as it flows through the unseen channels of our bodies at the rate of about five quarts a minute—and it describes only a fraction of what we already know of its tasks.

In certain respects, human life is a fragile, tenuous thing. It can, for instance, only exist within a very narrow range of temperature. Here the blood gives us a vital cushion of protection. As the major regulator of the body's heat, it strives at all times to provide us with the average temperature of 98.6° Fahrenheit, at which the human body is best suited to operate.

Even as it regulates the internal temperature of the body, the river of life has a key part in maintaining our internal fluid environment. Without moisture any life form, from the single cell to the most complex structure, ceases to function. But moisture is not enough. It must also contain certain chemical salts without which the fundamental life processes would be impossible.

Our blood, and related fluids such as the lymph, actually constitute the internal environment of our bodies. Just as the air is our external environment, flowing over our outer surfaces and carrying off heat and wastes exuded through our pores and lungs, these fluids constantly bathe the internal surfaces of our bodies. Able to pass through the cell walls, they help feed the cells and carry off wastes. So great is their importance that any serious loss of these body fluids could quickly produce what we know as shock and, unless the shock is relieved, death.

Another of the vital functions of the blood is the transport of those mysterious biochemical messengers—the hormones—which regulate the countless activities of the body. These potent chemicals are involved in the manifold processes of life. The hormones serve us in conception, birth, growth, love and joy. They influence our mental activities, our intelligence, our instincts and our emotions. When needed, they may even stimulate the fear, anger or intense concern which could, in a moment of dire emergency, provide a burst of life-saving energy.

Probably one of the least-understood tasks of the blood is its defense of the body's health. It stands as a constant bulwark against invasion by the swarms of microbes that infest our environment. Without the serried defenses provided by our blood, we probably could not survive a single day against the assaults of our microscopic foes.

The mysteries of the blood's defenses are slowly beginning to be unraveled. We know that the blood provides various specialized as well as general defenses against disease organisms. We all know something of the phagocytes, the white cells of the blood which hunt down and, literally, eat invading microbes. These spring to the defense of the body as soon as it is invaded and are carried to the area under attack by the blood or lymph.

In addition to the phagocytes, substances known as antibodies come to the body's defense. Antibodies fight specific disease organisms to which the body has been exposed. Unlike the phagocytes, which are non-discriminating soldiers attacking any foreign substance that invades the body tissue, the antibodies are active against only a single type of invader and, as far as this particular invader is concerned, are more efficient than the phagocytes.

But the antibodies are not the last of the defenses provided by the blood. Recently we have discovered in the protein fractions of the blood, the globulins, a protein called properdin which seems to have a positive effect on that phenomenon known as natural immunity—our ability to withstand disease though we may be constantly exposed to disease-causing organisms.

We are barely on the threshold of understanding properdin and its associated blood substances and the part they play in warding off disease. But the outlook is filled with promise. Experiments by scientists at Western Reserve University, the Sloan-Kettering Institute and other research centers indicate that these little-known chemicals may bolster our natural immunity to cancer, radiation disease and a host of other afflictions. This is by no means proved, and much work remains to be done before scientists can reach general agreement on the place of properdin in immunity.

Even with this we are nowhere near the end of the many wondrous functions performed by our blood. The river of life not only regulates itself and the body in which it flows, it is also self repairing. In some manner, which we are on the verge of understanding, the blood acts to prevent its own loss. If there is a cut or other wound that results in bleeding, the blood promptly reacts by creating a web-like substance known as fibrin. This is deposited over the wound and, by trapping cells from the blood, forms a clot which seals the opening through which the blood is escaping. Even the tiniest cut or pinprick may destroy hundreds of the microscopic capillaries which carry blood to the cells. Almost immediately, construction of replacement capillaries begins.

Probably one of the most fascinating of the blood's many tasks —all of which are directed to the single end of maintaining life— is the one which involves the transport of the important red cells. These cells carry oxygen from the lungs to the body cells, and remove carbon dioxide from the cells to the lungs. This unique ability to carry oxygen in one direction and carbon dioxide in the other is made possible by the properties of the hemoglobin, an iron-containing protein substance which gives these cells their red color.

In the six or so quarts of blood contained in the average adult body there are about 30 trillion of these cells. They are formed mainly in the bone marrow, and their birth and death rates are fantastically high—some 75 million red cells are born and die every minute. Red cells survive about 120 days and, when they become aged or damaged, are removed by special scavenger cells in the liver. They are then destroyed and eliminated, but most of the vital iron in the hemoglobin—so absolutely essential to oxygen transport—is salvaged and returned to the bone marrow where it is used again to form the hemoglobin of newly-constructed blood cells.

Since the average diet does not provide sufficient iron to replace that involved in the normal destruction of red cells, this iron-salvaging operation is actually a life-saving economy without which anemia and death would certainly result.

The development of our circulatory system was no logical, step-by-step progression. Spurred by apparently random mutation, environmental change and the shifting variables of natural selection, evolution does not always follow a straight line. And we should recognize that there is as much order in a jungle as there is in a carefully-tended grove—only it is a different kind of order and more difficult to comprehend.

The number of mutations that arose since the appearance of the first cell is literally beyond imagination. A single-cell staphylococcus which divides each hour, under ideal conditions produces about 300 billion staphylococci in 48 hours. If we calculate that only one of these in a million is a mutant, then 300 million mutants are produced in a mere two days. How, then, can we number the possible mutations in three thousand million years?

Out of thousands of possible mutations, each one of which may result from some random effect of the environment upon the genetic material of the cell, one may be progressive enough to improve the ability to survive. Most significant mutations are defects rather than improvements. They are quickly obliterated.

The total number of mutational errors that passed into oblivion before our circulatory system evolved is much too vast to comprehend. Yet virtually each step in that evolution is visible in the world around us. The first living thing to appear on earth was probably not much different from the single-celled amoeba which still takes sustenance from the fluid around it.

The open-canal system of circulation can be seen in the sponge. This type of circulation, while useful, is not particularly efficient since it does not permit the organism to vary its environment to any great degree. Yet, for creatures anchored to rocks and other fixed positions, canal circulation has maintained life through many millions of years to the present day.

The earliest closed system of circulation, in which the fluids were contained within, can be seen in such primitively organized plants as algae and certain seaweeds, as well as in such forms of animal life as the sea anemone. Here life-essential substances and wastes are passed to and from the cells without distinct canals or tubes.

The next evolutionary step up the ladder of complexity can be seen in such animals as the jellyfish and in the more highly organized plants whose sap is equivalent to our blood. In them, the river of life flows through definite tubes or vessels, but these do not pulsate as do our arteries, nor is there a heart to drive the essential fluids through the system. At this stage of evolution, the vessels do not have valves to direct the flow of fluid and keep it moving in one direction. Instead, at different times and under different circumstances, the fluids may flow in one direction or in another, as needed. In trees, the sap may flow upward at one time of year, then down at a different season.

We can only make vague guesses as to the number of eons it took for the first insect to appear. But there we see a still higher form of circulation. There is, as yet, no heart. But the vessel carrying the vital fluid at last is able to pulsate, driving the river along its way.

It is in the fish that the heart appears—an organ with two chambers. Then comes the snake with a three-chambered heart. Finally, in birds and in mammals, the heart has evolved into an organ with four chambers—two auricles and two ventricles. The reason for the differences in something so basic as the heart makes interesting speculation.

Natural selection, complex though it might appear, operates with singular logic and economy. That which is more efficient survives more readily than that which is less efficient. That which operates efficiently with economy, survives more readily than that which operates equally well but with less economy.

The number of cavities or chambers in the heart depends, among other things, upon the complexity of respiration. In the fish, respiration is relatively simple. There are no lungs, and blood is aerated by the gills. Therefore one heart chamber, the ventricle, is able to pump the blood to the gills and, through them, into the system. The second chamber, the auricle, receives the blood returning from the system and passes it back into the ventricle.

The snake has lungs, but a less complex circulation than birds or mammals, so two auricles are needed to receive the blood from the lungs and system, but only one ventricle is needed to pump it out.

In birds and in mammals, respiration and circulation are complex. Therefore two auricles and two ventricles are required. One auricle receives venous blood from the system, passes it to a ventricle which pumps it into the lungs where it is aerated. The other auricle receives the aerated blood from the lungs and passes it to the other ventricle which pumps it back into the system.

The four-chambered heart, as it exists in man, his mammalian cousins and in his more distant relatives, the birds, is also a mark of the warm-blooded creature whose internal temperature remains relatively constant. The fish, snakes and other reptiles are cold-blooded—their internal temperatures vary with the temperature of the surrounding environment.

During the long period of increasing complexity and specialization that finally resulted in man, the surrounding sea not only became a river within—with all the intricate developments of the circulatory system that this implies—but the content of the river itself changed. Blood serum still is very much like the original sea, but the blood solids include many new substances.

The sea had no red cells to carry oxygen. These and a number of other elements in the blood developed through the ages to meet the challenge of natural selection. On the other hand, some living things, such as plants, do not have red cells in their circulating fluids because they do not require them for oxygen transport. In its substance and circulatory structure, the river of life has evolved through the ages to serve the specific needs of the particular form of life within which it flows.

The evolution of the blood can be seen in its similarities as well as in its differences. It has been shown by G. H. F. Nuttall that human blood and the blood of monkeys and the higher apes have somewhat similar reactions to certain tests. But as the apes become higher in the evolutionary scale, their blood reactions become more closely similar to those of man until, in the gorilla, chimpanzee and orang-utan, the results are about the same as in humans.

Of course, the size of the red cells may differ from creature to creature and there may be certain chemical differences. From the tiny, monkey-like lemur to man, the red cells become progressively larger until, in the chimpanzee, orang-utan and gorilla, the size is pretty much the same as in man. Furthermore, these large apes have the same four blood groupings—A, B, AB and O—that separate the main types of human blood.

Should we look back far enough, broadly enough and freely enough, we will find that we possess a degree of "blood relationship" not only with the apes and other mammals, but with virtually every living thing—even trees, birds, reptiles, fish, insects and flowers—in each of which some distant portion of the original sea still flows, just as it flows within ourselves.

Among mammals, whether they be wolves or whales, humans or hippopotami, the brotherhood of life is so close that for a brief period during gestation it is difficult to tell them apart. This is particularly true in the development of the blood and circulation in the embryo.

In all mammals, when the ovum has been fertilized, it is nourished through the fluids of the mother which pass around it, much as the first cell was nourished by the sea. Then, as the cells multiply, they form a rounded mass within which a fluid collects. The outer wall of this cell mass develops hair-like fringes known as *chorionic villi* which embed themselves in the mother's uterine tissue and absorb nourishment through the mother's blood.

The body of the embryo develops from three layers of germ cells within the growing mass of cells. It is from the middle layer, known as the *mesoderm*, that the blood, blood vessels and heart are formed along with the skeleton, muscles and some other structures.

Throughout its very early development, the embryo speeds through eons of evolution, vaguely recapitulating the forms taken by its ancestors from the very first cell. For a brief period it has the slits which, in a fish, develop into gills. The heart of the early embryo is a simple, tubular affair like that of a fish. This folds over and develops into what resembles the heart of a cold-blooded amphibian, the frog. Then, pushing up the ladder of evolution, the embryo develops the characteristics of the mammal.

When the human embryo is about six weeks old it takes on human characteristics which help distinguish it from other mammals. Even then, it still has a tail which does not begin to vanish until the seventh week.

By this time the embryo already has a primitive blood and circulatory system of its own. The blood cells, developing from certain "stem cells" that arose from the mesoderm, are already circulating. Each of these primitive stem cells becomes the ancestor of countless millions of mature blood cells.

The embryo, and the fetus into which it develops, neither eats nor breathes, so the nutrients and oxygen it requires must come through the mother. It is also through the mother that its wastes are carried away. The blood of the mother and the blood of the fetus never come into direct contact. They are parts of two separate systems. But they do establish an indirect contact in the placenta, a disc-shaped structure which is formed in the womb out of embryonic and maternal tissues, and which is later discharged as part of the afterbirth.

A rich supply of the mother's blood flows through the placenta, carrying nutrients and oxygen. These are passed through the delicate capillary walls and into the hair-like chorionic villi which then pass them into the blood vessels of the fetus. Meanwhile, carbon dioxide and other wastes are passed in the other direction, from the blood of the fetus into the blood of the mother.

The blood of the fetus is pumped by the fetal heart through two umbilical arteries leading to the placenta. The nourished and oxygenated blood then returns to the fetus by way of the umbilical vein which, coiled together with the two arteries, forms the umbilical cord. The blood from the placenta then circulates through the fetus, delivering vital materials, picking up wastes and then returning to the placenta once more where it is cleansed and enriched by its indirect contact with the blood of the mother.

It is not until the infant is born and takes its first few breaths that the course of its circulation changes to meet the needs of an independent, air-breathing organism. By this time, other rapidly-developing biological processes have caused the blood vessels of the umbilicus to shrink and become a solid cord.

In the human, this umbilical cord is tied off close to the infant's body, then cut—and a new being, sustained by its own river of life, has been born out of a mother that was once the sea.

THE River of Life

Part One THE Magic River

Chapter One The Magic of Blood

Primitive man saw danger everywhere—around, above, below and even within.

There was danger in the air, in the forests, in the caves, in the marshes, in the grasslands, in the skies, in the waters. There was danger in the light and in the dark, in the heat and in the cold, in the sounds and in the silence. And, to the dangers of the world he knew, were added the imaginary dangers that filled the world of his vast ignorance.

He could, from his own hunger, understand the rapacity of the beasts that attacked him. But he had neither the experience nor knowledge to understand the lightning, the storms, the maiming fall of a tree limb, the slide of rock that might bury him in his cave, the quick flooding of a stream, or the rumbling of the earth beneath his feet. To him, it was plain that he was completely surrounded by demoniac powers.

Early man—including *homo sapiens* as well as the other forms of man that have since become extinct—sought desperately for any means that might give him the slightest additional measure of security, an extra mouthful of food, one more day of life. Within the narrow limits of his vision there was only one way for him to turn and that was to the supernatural which, in the absence of knowledge, provided a means of "explaining" the apparently unexplainable. Since this required only faith, it was in no way limited by ignorance.

Once man defined the forces around him in terms of the supernatural, his next step was to attempt to influence them. This became the function of magic, the "science and technology" of the supernatural. Only primitive man naturally did not see magic in our terms; nor was it supernatural, for in his dark world the natural and the supernatural were one.

At the very dawn of human consciousness, man grasped that blood and life were tightly intertwined. Primitive man was a hunter. He knew that when any living thing was wounded, blood flowed. When life was gone, the blood stopped flowing. Even if a creature died from drowning, lightning, disease or a blow that caused no bleeding; when the creature was opened, no blood flowed. Clearly, the property of life somehow resided in the mysterious red fluid. Thus, blood—which was so intimately involved with life—became life. And red, the color of blood, took on its properties and, by extension, the properties of life. From man's very first essay into the magical control of his world, the most potent "force" at his disposal has undoubtedly been blood. Consequently, our knowledge of blood has been colored by magical concepts often disguised as philosophy, theology or science.

Blood was life and life was blood. In Deuteronomy (12:23) it is declared: ". . . the blood is the life . . ." Life is man's most precious possession and, since that life resided in the blood, the greatest offering man could make to the demons of his shadowy world was the gift of blood.

If a shortage of meat brought the threat of starvation, perhaps the demon who had frightened away the game could be appeased by an offering of blood. Blood might be poured into a stream to calm the angry force that made it flood. Blood could be spilled to still the fury of the earthquake.

Out of the assumption that blood is life, other beliefs flowed directly and logically. If blood held the "life force," a man could add to his own life by drinking blood, rubbing it upon himself or performing other rites with it. The belief in vampirism, which still exists in backward corners of the world, can be traced to this idea.

It was also reasonable for man to believe that, since the strength, ferocity, fleetness, cunning and other qualities of a creature existed only during life, these properties resided in the "life force" contained within the blood. Therefore, if a man wanted the strength of a mammoth, he might acquire some by drinking the blood of a mammoth; the blood of a sabre-toothed tiger might give him ferocity and courage; the blood of a hawk might sharpen his vision. Or drinking the blood of another man might endow him with that man's abilities.

When a Scythian warrior killed his first man in battle, he drank the victim's blood to absorb his vitality. The present-day African Masai, by drinking the blood of a lion, believes he acquires the lion's strength and courage. Christian Friedrich Garmann, a physician of 17th century Germany, wrote of a young girl who acquired feline characteristics by drinking the blood of a cat. And in 17th century England, Yorkshire peasant women believed they could increase their fecundity by drinking the blood of an enemy.

Where man's needs were approximately the same, the patterns of his thought and reaction did not vary greatly. Were we to give a wheel to a Lake-Dweller of prehistoric Europe, another to an isolated Bushman of the Kalihari and still another to a man of Stone Age Java, they would probably find a similar, if not identical, use for it. It was the same way with blood magic.

None of this was much different from the drinking of wine in the early Greek rites for Dionysus, God of the Vine. Through an extension of imitative magic, the red juice of the grape came to represent the blood of the god and, by drinking the wine, the Greeks were partaking of Dionysian blood and thus sharing in his divinity. In many religions it was common practice to share in the divinity of a god by drinking his blood, actually or symbolically.

Imitative magic was a logical extension of direct magic. It is based on the belief that things which are similar in appearance share the same properties. In voodoo, for instance, the image of a person is identical with the person and, by burning the effigy or piercing it with a thorn, the person it represents is equally injured. To this very day some of us, often unknowingly, still practice forms of imitative magic when we hang someone in effigy or kiss the photo of a loved one.

Very early man believed that red, the color of blood, had the magical powers of blood. Archeological findings indicate that Cro-Magnon man painted the sick and dead red, presumably hoping to provide them with the "life force" contained within the blood and, in this way, either cure the sick or restore the dead to some future life.

In early Egypt, the practice of anointing one's self with blood to ward off illness and evil, quickly gave way to imitative magic. The Egyptians painted their nails red and made red pastes and pomades which they rubbed on their faces and bodies. As the years passed, this came to be accepted as a form of personal decoration and beautification.

Anything colored red, a ribbon, flower, berry, even a robe, could serve as a substitute for blood in a wide number of charms and rites. Red bed coverings were used to treat smallpox in early England. In 19th century London, strips of red cloth were sold as a cure for scarlet fever. Many modern Europeans, like the ancient Chinese and the present-day Maoris of New Zealand, will wear a red ribbon, ring, necklace or other article as a defense against evil and disease.

Ancient superstition persists even into the most modern areas.

Many of our pills and medicines are colored red, although the coloring plays absolutely no medicinal role. While the pharmaceutical and cosmetics manufacturers can hardly be considered practitioners of imitative blood magic, ancient traditions and habits often outlive our memory of the reasons that gave them birth.

An expanding series of beliefs and practices proceeded directly out of the original magical assumptions. As these became more complex and ritualized they evolved into religions. There is little doubt that the substance of primitive magic, savage as it seems to us today, made it possible for our ancestors to face their world with greater assurance and so helped them survive its hardships.

Throughout most of our history, particularly our early history, the bulk of our knowledge was wrenched out of necessity. When early man was faced with an emergency, he either knew how to face it or he died. Sometimes he did both.

Long before the first permanent village was built, man—in addition to hunting—had been gathering wild nuts, berries, fruits and grains for food. Gradually he discovered that there were ways to work the soil and cultivate the food-producing plants. When he realized that the soil could be made to provide food even when there was no game, man settled on the land and created new magic rituals to ensure the success of the crops.

Many mysterious forces had to be propitiated. There had to be enough water, but not too much. There had to be enough sun, but not too much. Great winds and storms had to be kept at a safe distance. Then, beyond all of these was the greatest mystery of all—the cycle of life into death and death into life.

This mystery was everywhere and affected everything. Man had only to look about him and he could see the continuity of life and death. Each morning the sun was born out of the earth in the east. Each evening the sun perished and returned into the earth in the west. After a night of entombment, the sun was reborn again as part of the continuous mystery of death and resurrection. All this was obvious to anyone who could see.

As it was with the godlike sun which provided light and warmth, so was it with all things that lived, and especially with the grain. In the spring the seed was planted. In the summer it grew and came to ripeness. After the harvest of maturity, came winter and death. But each new spring brought the miracle of rebirth. What the earth had claimed in death, became the substance of the vernal resurrection.

Primitive man's first interpretation of the cycle of birth, growth, death and rebirth has had immeasurably profound influence down to the present day. It was only natural for man's own concept of a life after death to be an extension of the same life, death and rebirth cycle he saw in the rising and setting of the sun, in the growing and dying of the crops and in the coming, going and returning of the seasons.

Since the growth of food became essential to life, the magic rituals designed to assure the success of the crops involved that most potent life force of all, the blood. Among people who lived by tilling the soil, it was an almost universal practice to offer up blood sacrifices when the time came for spring sowing. Blood was poured into the furrows where the seed was to be planted, blood was mixed with earth and seed, the seeds were dipped in blood.

As the magical rites developed into religions, the blood mysteries were acted out in greater and more intricate detail. In some early tribes, the chief or king, who was also the priest or an incarnation of the god, was killed each year and his blood and flesh used to replenish the life in the soil.

After the deaths of many kings, a symbolic practice was developed in many separate parts of the world. Each year, a man—generally a youth of outstanding physical qualities—was selected to become the incarnation of the god. Then, after a period during which he lived as his tribesmen imagined a god should live, he was sacrificed at the sowing or harvest festival and his blood offered to the soil.

In many lands and over many millennia, variations of this annual blood rite were religiously observed. Among the very early Egyptians, the god Osiris perished at each year's sowing festival. Red-haired men were first selected to represent him; later, red oxen were substituted for human sacrifices. With the passage of time, the tradition was satisfied when effigies of the god were buried. In this way, the Egyptians believed, the god gave his own body both as a scapegoat for man's transgressions and to produce food for his people. So each year he died that they might live, and each year he was resurrected with the growing grain.

In ancient Mexico and Peru, a steady stream of sacrifices provided blood to assure each year's crop. Among the Mexicans, infants were sacrificed as the corn was sown. When it sprouted, older children were offered up. Finally, when the corn was fully ripe and ready for harvest, old men were sacrificed.

Even in Europe the soil was nourished with human blood and, to this day, vestiges of early rites remain in the festivities which are observed on the first day of May. The annual King and Queen of the May represent victims who were sacrificed each year.

From prehistoric times down to the present day, magical blood lore has been involved in profound mysteries, in tender romances, in strange rites and even in unspeakable cruelties. Many modern beliefs and practices reach back into the ancient magic of the blood. Circumcision, now credited with having sound medical reasons, is an outgrowth of primitive blood sacrifice. There are indications that among primitive tribes the firstborn son was sometimes offered as a sacrifice, possibly for continued fertility. Apparently, this sacrifice later became symbolized in the almost universal rite of circumcision in which a small amount of blood was spilled. Today, the sacrificial origins of circumcision have been largely forgotten and, as is frequently the case, eminently modern and medically satisfactory reasons have been found for a very ancient ritual.

According to Genesis, circumcision dates back to Abraham's

covenant with God. Its Hebrew name, significantly, is *brith dam* —blood covenant. Actually, the rite of circumcision is even more ancient than the Hebrews and originated independently among many peoples of the world. It was practiced in predynastic Egypt long before Abraham could have lived, according to the noted Egyptologist, Professor Elliot Smith. The early Phoenicians practiced circumcision of their young males. American Indian and African tribes performed circumcision, as do the Moslems. While most Moslems are circumcised at puberty, among a few tribes the rite is performed the day after a young man is married. Some of the blood is then sprinkled on the veil of the bride—possibly as some ancient exchange for the hymeneal blood she sacrificed with her virginity.

One of the most persistent of the myths involving blood—and one that has taken an incredible human toll—is the belief that the blood not only contains life but also the qualities of a being. We still refer to people of "good" character as having "good" blood, people of "bad" character as having "bad" blood. This is more than a mere misuse of words. Relatively recent philosophers no less than primitive man, actually believed that a portion of the blood of the parent was transmitted to the child and thus passed from generation to generation. In this way the actual blood of Wotan and Thor was supposed to be present in the veins of modern Germans.

Through some mystical property, blood presumably carried the essence of the individual, the family, the clan, the nation and the race. Semantic and physiological nonsense about Irish, Polish, American and other "national" blood is still current. People speak of white or negro blood; of Jewish, Protestant, Catholic or Moslem blood. The concepts underlying these common beliefs arise from the same fears and ignorance which first gave birth to primitive superstition.

In our own day, these beliefs reached their most vicious climax with the absurd myth of Aryan blood. Aryan actually refers to neither race nor nation but to a group of languages including

Persian, Sanskrit and Greek among others. So, in the 20th century, a prehistoric misconception, distorted and falsely applied, was used to help justify a systematic slaughter which would have been beyond the imagination of our savage ancestors.

Less lethal misconceptions arising from primitive blood lore abound in our language and in our beliefs. We often speak of hot or cold-blooded people, referring to their temperament or their ability to withstand temperature changes. We describe people as full-blooded or half-blooded referring to the degree of racial, religious or national intermixture. We even speak of royal blood, although this concept arose out of the belief that the essence of divinity from the first God-King was passed down through the blood of kings.

The idea of "blue" blood has been attributed to Castilian nobles who called it *sangre azul* to indicate that they were free of the supposedly darker blood of the Moors. Blue blood actually exists, though it has nothing to do with social status or cast. The blood that flows through the veins has a bluish cast, imparted by carbon dioxide and other wastes, as compared with the bright red of arterial blood.

Like so many other blood superstitions, the mystical belief that the blood held the soul of an individual and perpetuated special qualities, leaped across space and time. Among varying cultures in widely scattered parts of the world, this belief produced similar practices. Blood compacts date from ancient times virtually to the present. Alliances, brotherhood, friendship and other relationships were established by some exchange of blood. So-called compacts with the devil were said to be signed in blood. Blood was used as a "cure" or "treatment" for spells, bewitchings or ailments. Greeks, Medes and Persians, according to Herodotus, would cement an alliance by cutting their arms and licking each others blood. In other ceremonies, the hands were cut and then held or tied together so that the blood would intermingle. It may well be that our present custom of shaking hands to mark an agreement developed from this practice of sealing a covenant in blood.

The magic of blood is very much with us, reaching through our thoughts, our language, our religion, our relationships, our art, our literature and even our science. The blood superstitions that arose from man's first fearful ignorance still exert a potent influence. Neither time nor civilization have destroyed all of the old blood rituals. Some, such as circumcision, have been found useful in the light of modern medical knowledge. In such cases, attempts are often made to impute this modern knowledge to the ancients. This, by implication, can become a defense of other, less useful, relics of our superstitious past.

Other rites, such as the partaking of the blood and flesh of a god, have become highly symbolized through imitative magic. In those cases, the primitive logic-through-ignorance out of which the original magic arose has been cloaked in metaphysical garb to flourish safe from the challenge of scientific inquiry.

In the very beginning, man's discovery of the magic of blood provided him with a psychological weapon which helped him pass safely through the terrors of his dawn world. Today, even from the vantage point of the Nuclear Age, it would be well for us to acknowledge the transcendental importance of that achievement. As man's first attempt to understand, explain and influence his environment, primal magic was to become the mother of our science.

Chapter Two

The Forbidden Blood

In various tribal societies all over the world, in Haiti and other Caribbean islands, in Europe and the more backward parts of the southern United States, men and women still sicken and die from voodoo, the "evil eye" or some other form of curse. There are no medically detectable reasons for their decline.

Magical deaths were even reported as recently as June 28, 1957 to England's Royal Society of Medicine. In a paper delivered to the Section of Obstetrics and Gynecology, Dr. Francis Camps of the London Hospital Medical College declared that there had been some unexplained deaths among negro women who had been coming to England in large numbers. Three of these cases, he said, could only be attributed to such mysterious forces as "ju-ju."

This does not "prove" the reality of magic but emphasizes the somatic power of psychic conviction—a phenomenon which can be demonstrated experimentally upon hypnotic subjects. The body mechanisms of a subject will often react to the suggestion of cold, for instance, just as though the cold were real. Goose pimples form, the subject shivers, his teeth chatter and actual changes take place in the circulation as the body responds to the hypnotic suggestion with a very real reaction.

To our primitive ancestors, magic and reality were part of the same fabric of existence. They used sorcery just as they would use a spear, a stone ax or a digging stick. These were all tools which could help man achieve certain desired results—a successful hunt, victory in battle, a safe journey.

But there were certain dangers which man could not overcome with any of his tools, real or magical. The only way to survive these perils was to avoid them. Thus arose the rules of avoidance —the taboos—which have been called humanity's oldest unwritten code of laws. It was from these early taboos that much of our ethical systems and religions ultimately evolved.

The taboos were based on negative magic. One did not do a certain thing for fear of terrible consequences. The mechanism of taboo can be seen in many present day superstitions. Do not break a mirror lest seven years misfortune befall you. Do not cross knives while setting a table lest you become involved in a quarrel.

A variety of acts and objects were covered by taboos, all of them containing some element of natural or supernatural danger. But the most fertile source of taboo, according to the philosopher-psychologist Wilhelm Max Wundt, was man's attempt to avoid demoniac powers which could neither be allayed nor controlled.

With magic so pervasive a factor in the life and death of early man, and with the blood recognized as one of the most potent of all magical forces, blood's power for evil was held almost as great as its potential for good. Just as the right blood, properly used, could bring life, strength or good fortune, the wrong blood —or blood improperly used—could bring disaster. So, almost from the outset of man's attempts to influence his environment, there arose the laws of the forbidden blood—the fear-rooted complex of blood taboos.

We can only guess at the very earliest taboos. Later taboos can be estimated by studying contemporary primitive peoples such as the Australian and African bushmen and the American Indians whose native culture has not emerged from the Stone Age.

Many taboos developed as societies evolved and created new social pressures. Emerging groups and classes—kings, priests and nobles—created and imposed taboos designed to protect themselves and their powers. As an example, speaking the Holy Name of God or entering into some Holy of Holies was often taboo to all but a priest, thus assuring the power of the priesthood as intermediary between man and his particular God. Vestiges of other taboos can be seen in our religions today and even in the normally accepted relationships and attitudes of modern life. The taboo against incest is one of the oldest and most widespread in human experience.

One of the most fascinating and mysterious aspects of taboo is its ability to leap both space and time. Similar, indeed almost identical, taboos have prevailed among widely separated peoples. As with blood magic, the identity of blood taboos must have arisen out of humanity's relatively common response to a common need at a common level of cultural development.

While many peoples believed that desirable qualities could be acquired by drinking the blood of creatures possessing those qualities, others tabooed the drinking of blood for much the same reason. Among peasants of the Eastern Baltic, and certain North American Indian tribes, blood was long taboo as food lest the eater become possessed by the spirit of the animal from which it came. Similarly, early Jewish hunters had to pour out the blood of the game they killed lest it be eaten.

The Jewish taboo against blood is clearly defined in the Old Testament: "And whatsoever man there be of the children of Israel, or of the strangers that sojourn among you, which hunteth and catcheth any beast or fowl that may be eaten; he shall even pour out the blood thereof, and cover it with dust." (Lev. 17:13) The life force, imparted by God, belongs to God and must be returned to Him. Whoever violated this taboo faced dire punishment: "For the life of all flesh is in the blood thereof; whosoever eateth it shall be cut off." (Lev. 17:14)

This taboo is still observed by orthodox people of Jewish faith, for the ritual of making meat *kosher* is designed to remove its blood.

The Mosaic taboo against the eating of blood was incorporated into both Christian and Islamic tenets. According to the New Testament, the council of apostles and elders of the church, meeting in Jerusalem to decide certain matters under dispute, such as whether circumcision was necessary to salvation, reached the following decision:

"For it seemed good to the Holy Ghost, and to us, to lay upon you no greater burden than these necessary things;

"That ye abstain from meats offered to idols, and from blood, and from things strangled, and from fornication: from which, if ye keep yourselves, ye shall do well." (Acts, 15:28,29)

In Al Koran, the Holy Book of Islam, Mohammed included a remarkably similar injunction:

"He has made forbidden to you only carrion, blood, swine's flesh and that which has been offered to any other than Allah . . ." (Sura 16)

As tribal societies became more stable and the power of the god-kings became greater, taboos were created to forbid the spilling of royal blood upon the earth. This reversed the ancient practice of sacrificing the king each year and using his blood to ensure the fertility of the soil and to expunge the sins of his people.

Even where a king or someone else of royal lineage was put to death, the blood was collected with great care because if even a drop of it fell to earth it would become defiled. Since this royal blood was presumed to contain the essence of tribal divinity, any violation of the taboo would visit misfortune upon the tribe.

The taboo against permitting blood to fall upon the ground was observed in many places and for a variety of reasons. In ancient Peking, at the time of Marco Polo's visit to China, the letting of any blood was considered evil. Consequently, when criminals were punished they were beaten with sticks, great care being taken not to break the skin and thus spill blood. Even the death penalty was carried out with the greatest concern for the protection of the blood.

There was a sharp and basic fear underlying the taboo against allowing blood to fall to the ground, leaving it unprotected. Since the blood was believed to carry the spirit of the individual as well as the mystic essence of the clan or tribe, great harm might come to the individual and even the tribe should this blood come into the hands of an enemy. The spirit within the blood might be imprisoned, enslaved or tortured; or an image might be made on which the blood might be dabbed, then horrible wounds inflicted upon this image. The agony and even death caused by these wounds might be visited upon the unfortunate who, by violating taboo, had permitted his blood to fall into evil hands.

Fearful of exposing their blood to possible havoc, primitive people almost everywhere developed strict, protective taboos. In parts of West Africa, if even a single drop of a man's blood fell to the ground, it had to be carefully covered with soil and then stamped into the earth so that it was obliterated. If the blood fell on a tree trunk, a canoe or the side of a hut, the place it spattered had to be cut out and destroyed. In West Sussex, writes anthropologist Sir James Frazer in *The Golden Bough*, it was believed that ground upon which human blood fell would be forever barren.

The most grotesque expression of the taboo against exposing one's blood was found in Madagascar. Nobles of the Betsileo tribe each had a slave called a *ramanaga* with very curious and personal duties.

A *ramanaga* followed his master everywhere he went and, if the noble spilled any blood whatsoever—whether from a pin prick, a wound or even a nosebleed—the *ramanaga* licked it up as swiftly as possible so that not the slightest trace remained for the spells of sorcerers. In addition to protecting his master's blood in this digestive fashion, the *ramanaga* also ate the noble's nail parings which could be used as instruments of magic.

Even today, in some tribal societies of Australia and New Guinea, it is forbidden to allow the blood of a tribesman to fall upon the ground lest the blood of the whole tribe become contaminated. Therefore when tribal blood must be spilled, as during circumcision or some other ritual, the subject is held aloft so his blood may be caught on the bodies of his fellow tribesmen.

As far back as we can probe into man's history and wherever on earth he has lived—on the shores of a European lake, in the gloomy stillness of some rain forest or in the vast tundras of the

Arctic—the most stringent taboos have been those inspired by menstruation and imposed on women. Furthermore, there is a sameness about these taboos wherever they exist. It is almost as though they arose at that distant time when man first appeared and before, as some believe, he branched out to cover the earth. Or perhaps they are one more example of mankind's generally similar responses to similar situations.

The universal fear of menstrual blood was rooted in the logic of magic. In primitive man's world of demons and sorcery, it seemed reasonable that anything as precious as blood—which was life itself—would be cherished and preserved. Therefore any blood that was rejected by the body—as was menstrual blood and the blood of childbirth—must be unlike the blood of life. This could only be a different blood, containing evil spirits, restless demons, inner defilement and great power to do harm.

The coincidental similarity between the menstrual and lunar cycles was a factor in providing magical and religious overtones to menstruation. Many primitive peoples believed (and still believe) that the menses are a blood sacrifice demanded by the moon. This idea has persisted in poetry, in literature and even in theology. The 19th century French theologian, Villaret, declared that, because of her high destiny, Joan of Arc was "exempt from the tribute women pay to the moon."

The philosophers of ancient Babylon held that the red appearance of the moon at wane was due to the blood of the Moon Goddess, Istar, who was presumably having her period at that time. Among tribesmen in Papua, it was believed that girls were seduced by the moon, and it was this rape that brought on the bleeding.

It is still widely accepted, even in relatively civilized circles, that each month a woman's menstrual flow washes out poisonous substances and harmful bacteria which accumulate in her body. We are supposed to know better, but, by some peculiar working of human demonolatry, old prejudices and superstitions tend to persist in the face of the facts that refute them.

In recent years psychoanalysts and psychoanalytically oriented anthropologists, following a somewhat complex path of subtle indirection, have attempted to explain the reasons underlying the widespread taboo of menstrual blood.

The eminent anthropologist Robert H. Lowie suggests that man's extreme horror of menstrual blood may actually be an expression of hidden awe and admiration. A similar view is advanced by Dr. Bruno Bettelheim in his fascinating book, *Symbolic Wounds.* While we all have general attitudes of anxiety toward the loss of blood, Bettelheim writes, some psychoanalysts believe that we see in menstrual blood a visible sign of female sexual maturity and the ability to bear children. And since the male has no equivalent sign of sexual maturity, menstruation tends to arouse admiration and envy in him. It was out of this submerged envy, according to this theory, that the menstrual taboos were established. According to George Devereux, an anthropologist as well as psychoanalyst, the menstrual taboos were designed as a form of homage to women who, having the power to create new life from their bodies, must be set apart from the rest of mankind as sacred.

Regardless of the possible motivations of our primal ancestors, the belief did emerge that the menstruating female is charged with a powerful force that must be tightly contained lest it prove destructive to herself and to all around her. It was to imprison this force and thus protect the safety of all concerned, that the menstrual taboos were imposed.

Virtually everywhere on earth women were taboo during their periods, during childbirth and especially during puberty. They were thought to be so dangerous that primitive peoples quarantined menstruating women in tabooed huts or isolated areas. Anything they touched or even looked upon might be infected or destroyed.

The Babylonians, the Greeks and the Jews all imposed taboos upon menstruating women. In virtually every case, any contact with such a woman was considered polluting. The Bible decreed that any man who knowingly had carnal relations with a menstruating woman should be put to death (Lev. 18:19,29). According to the Talmud, the body of Jewish civil and canonical law, should a woman at the onset of her period pass between two men, she thereby kills one of them.

Menstruating women of tribal Australia were forbidden, upon pain of death, from touching anything used by men, from walking on a path used by men or from even looking at a man. Her touch, her glance and the aura of her presence were considered deadly to men.

Similar taboos were held by Indian tribes in North and South America. Among some, the glance of a menstruating woman was so dangerous to a man that she had to wear a special covering over her face. In South Africa, the Bushmen believed that a single glance from a woman in menstruation could turn a man into a tree. And the Laplanders barred menstruating women from walking near any part of a shore that might be used for fishing.

Cattle-raising tribes of Africa forbade a menstruous woman from drinking milk lest the cow that gave it die. And if a drop of her blood were to fall on the ground, any cattle that passed over it would die. For this reason, women—whether they were menstruating or not—were often forbidden to use any path over which cattle might pass. Instead, they were restricted to narrow back trails both inside and outside the village.

Australian aborigines secluded their women during childbirth. These women could not return to the normal life of the tribe until they had been cleansed and purified. The clothing, utensils and other things a woman used during her seclusion had to be burned or buried.

Women of some Indian tribes of Alaska, when they approached the time of delivery, were confined in reed huts where they had to remain for twenty days after giving birth. During this taboo period, a woman was believed so unclean and dangerous that none might touch her or come close to her. Food was thrust into her hut at the end of a long pole.

It is significant that in England and the United States today, the period surrounding a woman's childbearing is known as her "confinement." And in many parts of the civilized world there is that uneasy tendency to feel that men should stay "outside" when a mother is being delivered of her child.

Purification of a woman after childbirth was a very serious matter among the early Jews. If she gave birth to a boy, she was unclean for seven days and had to continue the rite of purification for 33 days thereafter, during which period she was forbidden to come into the sanctuary or touch any hallowed object. Girl infants evidently caused greater impurity than did boys. The mother of a girl was unclean for two weeks and then continued "in the blood of her purifying" for 66 more days (Leviticus, 12).

Even more lethal than the blood of childbirth was the blood of miscarriage. And if a woman concealed a miscarriage, her blood became so dangerous that, among the Bantu for instance, she was considered capable of spreading terrible infection.

Not only was the woman's husband threatened with death by the blood of a concealed miscarriage, but the whole country and even the sky itself was endangered. No rain would fall. The land would become hot, parched and barren. Food would cease to grow and there would be only desert.

The fear of menstrual blood and the blood of childbirth was great, but most dreaded and taboo of all was the blood of puberty. Since it was the product of a girl's initial menstrual period, it contained the pent-up demoniac powers which, being released for the first time, were more dangerous than ever afterward.

The terror of this blood was so pervasive that it influenced the way of life of many primitive peoples and, to a degree, has reached into our own times. Puberty taboos were remarkably similar throughout the world. Apart from the seclusion itself, two basic principles were widely observed: the girls must neither touch the ground nor see the sun. The evil of her blood was so great that she must be suspended between heaven and earth lest either of them be polluted.

In Borneo, girls of certain tribes were confined for as long as seven years in tiny cells raised above the ground and into which no light could penetrate. North American Indians placed their girls in small cages which were completely covered so that neither the sun or fire could be seen. Some Indians of South America sewed pubescent girls into their hammocks and kept them suspended in darkness.

Similar taboos prevailed in Asia. Hindu girls reaching puberty were kept in a dark room for several days and forbidden to see the sun. And in Cambodia, a girl reaching puberty was said to "enter into the shade." She was confined to bed, under a mosquito net, for 100 days.

Among the Zulus and other South African people, at the onset of her first menses a girl must hide herself among the reeds of the nearest stream, not to be seen by men. She must also cover her head carefully with a blanket so the sun will not shine on her. After dark, she is secluded in a hut from which all light is barred and not even a fire is allowed. Leaves are strewn on the floor so her feet will not touch the ground.

On the South Pacific island of New Ireland, girls have been locked in small cages for as long as five years, shut off from all light and unable to set foot upon the ground.

In his *Natural History*, Pliny, the great Roman naturalist, compiled a list of dangers arising from menstrual blood that far exceeded anything conceived by so-called savages. The touch of a menstruous woman could, according to Pliny, turn wine to vinegar, blight crops, dim mirrors, rust iron, blunt knives and razors, cause miscarriages among farm animals and so on.

The great Swiss physician of the 16th century, Paracelsus—whose full name in its Latinized version was Philippus Aureolus Theophrastus Bombastus von Hohenheim—is remembered for the impetus he gave to the revival of Western medicine. Yet this same Paracelsus taught that the devil created fleas, spiders and all other insects out of the blood of menstruation.

Much of this superstition clings to the fabric of our civilization to this very day. Some people still believe that a menstruating woman can cause milk to curdle, beer or wine to spoil. Many women during their periods refrain from touching flowers lest they wither them. And many women still refer to their menstrual period as "the curse."

The feeling still survives that a woman in menstruation is somehow dangerous to the sick and should not be allowed near them. In some hospitals menstruating nurses are occasionally kept away from surgical patients.

Spanning the eons and the continents, man's fear of the forbidden blood has been as great a force as his belief in the magic blood. It helped give direction to his rituals, found a place in his ethical codes and religions, influenced his social structure, his history and his attempts to achieve a rational view of the world in which he lived.

It would be difficult to prove that these influences have weighed to the good; but, whatever value judgements we may put upon them, the force of their impact can in no way be minimized. After all, man has been under the influence of fear, ignorance and the subtle elaborations of superstition vastly longer than he has been exposed to rational science.

Chapter Three The Blood of Guilt

For those who believed that their family or tribal blood contained unique and magical properties, it was natural to defend this blood with religious ferocity. Here we can see the origin of the blood feud, blood guilt and blood revenge. When blood was spilled, members of the victim's family had to appease the blood by an act of revenge.

Usually it was the duty of the nearest relative to avenge the shedding of blood. Under Mosaic law (Deut. 19:11–13), this relative was called "the avenger of the blood" and the act carried the sanction of divine will. Blood feuds and blood revenge are common to this day on every continent inhabited by man. In Sardinia alone, they may take a toll of several hundred lives each year.

One of the most awesome of the blood's alleged powers was its supposed ability to accuse its violators and to exact vengeance. From early times, when a man took a life, he had to perform elaborate rites to protect himself from the retaliatory magic of the blood he had spilled. For it was through the blood that the spirit of the victim was released; and it could follow the killer, haunt him and bring about madness or death.

It was long believed that whoever saw a corpse—relative, friend or stranger—had to walk up and lay a hand upon it. He who failed to do this would be haunted by the ghost of the deceased. Behind this there hovered an even more ancient and much more enduring superstition—that a corpse would bleed at the approach or touch of its murderer. This superstition has played a part in the solution of murder mysteries, and was long a part of British legal practice. Because of this fearful belief, murder suspects occasionally refused to be confronted by the corpse and thus revealed their guilt. England's legal history, as we will see, holds many examples of heinous crimes thus solved by blood.

The power of the blood to accuse received divine sanction in the Bible. After Cain had murdered his brother, the Lord said to him: "What hast thou done? The voice of thy brother's blood crieth unto me from the ground." (Gen. 4:10)

Even so advanced a philosopher as Sir Francis Bacon who, in the 17th century, helped lay the basis for modern science, wrote in his *Sylva Sylvarum*, a compilation of ten centuries of knowledge in the field of natural history:

"It is an usual observation, that if the body of one murthered be brought before the murtherer, the wounds will bleed afresh . . . It may be that this participateth of a miracle by God's just judgement, who usually brings murthers to light. . . ."

Bacon did not give unqualified endorsement to this belief. Yet, he had to take careful note of it. Here we have one of the wry ironies of our unfolding civilization. An error, a falsehood or some piece of sheer superstition which is generally accepted or believed, may be passed down unquestioned and untested through the generations. Each succeeding age accepts it as authoritative fact and thus further fortifies it as truth by the accretion of acceptance, until it is almost unthinkable even to question it.

Bacon probably read the early historical records which told of how blood flowed from the nostrils of dead King Henry II as his son Richard—later known as Coeur de Lion—approached the body. Richard, although he had not slain his father, had been in rebellion against him and thus involved in his death. So, according to the early accounts, the father's corpse bled in accusation at the approach of the son.

Equally bizarre is the story of Thomas, Earl of Lancaster, who was beheaded at Pontefract in 1322 and canonized in 1390. Thomas was held to be a martyr and a worker of miracles. The faithful who made pilgrimages to his tomb vowed they saw blood flow from it—a protest by the corpse against those who had cruelly and unjustly taken his life.

So thoroughly accepted was the belief in the accusatory power of the blood that in Europe, the British Isles and, indeed, over most of the world, it remained unquestioned until comparatively recent times. It even entwined itself into our folk stories, ballads and literature.

A Scottish ballad of old, entitled *Young Huntin*, describes how a man's blood exposed a woman's perfidy:

> O white, white were his wounds washen,
> As white as any clout;
> But when Lady Maisry she cam' near,
> The blood cam' gushing out.

The trial by blood of a maiden and a lady, both accused of murder, is described in *Earl Richard*, one of the ballads collected by Sir Walter Scott in his *Minstrelsy of the Scottish Border:*

> The maiden touched the clay-cauld corpse,
> A drap it never bled;
> The ladye laid her hand on him
> And soon the ground was red.

The ballad records that the maiden, thus proved guiltless by the corpse, was freed; but the "ladye," convicted by the evidence of the blood, was punished.

The evidence of the blood was accepted under the laws of William Shakespeare's time, which were apparently confirmed by the accumulations of history. It was quite natural, therefore, for Shakespeare to use this belief, as he did in *Richard the Third.*

In Act 1, Scene 2, as the body of Henry VI is being carried in solemn procession, Richard, the King's murderer, appears and halts the funeral proceedings. Lady Anne thereupon denounces him:

> ". . . If thou delight to view thy heinous deeds,
> Behold this pattern of thy butcheries.
> O, gentlemen, see, see! dead Henry's wounds
> Open their congealed mouths and bleed afresh!
> Blush, blush thou lump of foul deformity;

For 'tis thy presence that exhales this blood
From cold and empty veins where no blood dwells.
Thy deed, inhuman and unnatural,
Provokes this deluge most unnatural."

This scene did not spring entirely from Shakespeare's imagination. The flow of the dead king's blood had been accepted as a fact of England's gory past and had been so recorded by Raphael Holinshed, the noted chronicler of early English history.

"The dead corps. . . . was conueied. . . . from the Tower to the church of saint Paule, and there, laid on a beire or coffen bare faced, the same in the presence of the beholders did bleed: where it rested the space of one whole daie."

Mankind had come a long way from the fear-ridden savage to such enlightened men as Bacon and Shakespeare; yet the subtly tenacious bonds of superstition, embellished by the refinements of accumulating knowledge, reached across the ages to link them.

The strange belief regarding the accusatory power of blood remained a sturdy pillar of the law until the last century and was a powerful factor in the solution of many crimes.

In 1613, near Taunton in southwestern England, a widow was found brutally murdered. She had been stabbed 16 times.

The local magistrate summoned all the people in the vicinity—in this case, a radius of three miles—to appear before the corpse and touch it. All came except a man called Babb, a local citizen who had been wooing the widow. To the villagers, Babb's absence implied guilt, and a hue and cry was raised against him. Babb was pursued so relentlessly that he finally surrendered and confessed to the crime. He had murdered the widow in a storm of passion when she refused to marry him and, apparently fearing to touch the corpse, had fled.

Documents of the 17th century record the trial of Philip Standsfield for the murder of his father, Sir James, in 1688. At the inquest, presided over by Sir George McKenzie, testimony was produced to the effect that blood suddenly started to flow when the son touched his father's body. At this, the son had reportedly leaped back in horror, crying: "Lord have mercy on me!" This alleged testimony persuaded the jury that Philip Standsfield had indeed slain his father.

In 1828 Mr. John Dyon of Bancroft, England, was shot dead while on his way home from Doncaster Market. Since he had but recently prosecuted members of a gang of poachers, it was immediately suspected that this was a vengeance killing by members of the gang.

Meanwhile, a messenger was sent to the victim's brother, William Dyon, notifying him of the killing. William, as was generally known, had recently quarreled with his brother over the disposition of family property; but there was no evidence to link him with the crime and he was completely free from suspicion.

William came to the inquest, but when he entered the room where his brother's body was laid out he did not come near the corpse. Instead, he sought out the part of the room furthest away from the body, and closer than this he would not approach.

This odd behavior did not escape the notice of the others in the room. Some began to wonder whether William, unsuspected until that moment, was afraid to come close because he was somehow involved in the killing. The investigation shifted from the poachers to William, and it was soon confirmed that he and his son, John Jr., had indeed been implicated in the crime. They were tried, found guilty and subsequently hanged at York. An ancient superstition had led William to draw suspicion upon himself.

So, from earliest to relatively recent times, the blood judged suspects' guilt or innocence. Vestiges of this superstition remain to this very day. As we attend a funeral and file by the corpse in its open coffin, we are performing a ceremony which originated in the fearful times when death by violence was so often the rule. Passing close to the deceased, we are acting out that ancient trial by blood, with the corpse itself bearing witness to our guilt or innocence of possible murder.

Chapter Four

The Healing Blood

Life, by its very nature, shrinks from illness and pain. Each living thing, from the simplest, single-celled plant to man, possesses built-in mechanisms and responses designed to ward off sickness and injury and, should these fail, to attempt to heal itself.

Antibodies and immune mechanisms protect man and plant alike from infection; reflex responses cause both the human and the amoeba to pull back sharply from something dangerously hot. These are forms of innate self-protection that require neither awareness nor intelligence, only life. It is beyond this zone, across the threshold of conscious thought, that the art and science of healing begin.

Our pre-human ancestors unquestionably attempted to ease their hurts and ills. We know that monkeys will try to stop a wound from bleeding by placing a paw over the hurt and pressing upon it. Apes, dogs and other animals will show concern when their fellows are injured or ill and may even make some effort to help.

Man no less than the monkey has always attempted to ease his own hurts. But it was when he began to ease the hurts of others that the art of healing was born. Out of the art of healing, a science of healing took shape. This science has made tremendous strides in recent years but it has by no means fully emerged. Nor will it while medicine remains diluted by the influences of the supernatural which linger in many guises over much of the world.

According to the existing evidence, man's practice of the healing art was already well established some 20,000 years ago. Among the remarkable paintings in the caverns of the French Pyrenees is the representation of a man who was concerned with the treatment of the sick and injured. He is shown wearing the costume of his profession—a deer skin wrapped around his body, deer antlers on his head, fur mittens on his hands, a long beard on his face, the ears of a bear and the flowing tail of a horse. Thus appeared one of humanity's first doctors—the early Stone Age medicine man.

To the medicine man it must have been obvious that illnesses, infections and the various diseases could only have supernatural causes. Even wounds caused by animals, by accidents or in warfare could only have been inflicted because the victim's protective magic had failed him. And a cure could only be affected by marshaling supernatural forces on his behalf.

Accordingly, the task of the early doctor was largely a religious or supernatural one. Through spells, incantations, medicines made of herbs and other substances with "magically" curative powers, prayers and other rites he attempted to restore his patient to health by overcoming the inimical forces that beset him.

For many thousands of years the identity between religion and medicine persisted, and the only healers were priests or witch doctors with "access" to supernatural forces. Man learned by trial and error. When certain combinations of magical ritual, incantation and medicine seemed to work, they became established as treatment. If they failed, they were discarded. If they worked occasionally, the failures were attributed to some evil countermagic.

Out of this blind empiricism, man learned to use the vast majority of remedies still being prescribed today. These range all the way from tranquilizers such as rauwolfia to such powerful heart stimulants as digitalis. Even salycilates, today known as aspirin, were prescribed by witch doctors as a tea made from the bark of willow trees.

Of all the magical tools at the disposal of the witch doctor, the most potent instrument of healing was the blood. Since the blood was recognized as the equivalent of life, it was obviously death's greatest antagonist. And the evil demons of disease struck at life by invading the blood. Out of this theory of disease there arose an entire concept of healing that depended mainly upon the magical aspects of the blood.

We have already noted how red, the color of blood, was deemed to have blood's magical properties and how the Stone Age medicine men painted their sick and dead with red ochre in order to restore them. Similarly, the early Egyptians painted their gods red in order to keep them healthy. Through the thousands of years that medicine has been shackled to the supernatural, blood and any magical red colored counterpart were believed to contain great healing force.

Animal blood was used as medicine by the priest-physicians of ancient Egypt. Wealthy Romans drank the blood of slain gladiators as a cure for epilepsy. Menstrual blood was prescribed as a treatment for gout by Paracelsus, a great physician of the Middle Ages, while in Switzerland, Denmark and other parts of Europe, the blood of decapitated criminals was considered useful in the treatment of hydrophobia and consumption as well as epilepsy.

Blood was of great importance in the medicine practiced by the Druids and the later Anglo-Saxons. Anglo-Saxon physicians, influenced by Druidic lore, came to be called "Leeches" because of their widespread use of those bloodsucking creatures in their practice. The leeches, gorging themselves on the presumably demon-infected blood of the patient, were believed to draw off the disease and transfer it to themselves. Due to this early and almost universal form of bloodletting in medicine, doctors became known as Leeches, a name which occasionally clings to the present day.

Many of the Anglo-Saxon Leeches received their training at monastaries, which also served as clinics. Early drawings show the Anglo-Saxon Leech as a serious-faced man with a long beard and a full moustache. His general appearance, like that of the modern physician, was undoubtedly intended to inspire confidence and to convey an impression of great learning. He wore a tunic with a decorated border reaching to his knees and a decorated girdle. His legs were bare but over his feet he wore hose and soft boots with roll-down tops.

The treatments used by these physicians were appropriately called "leechdoms," and blood played an important part. A highly-regarded leechdom used in a great variety of internal ailments consisted of pellets made of clay mixed with the blood of goats and marked with a sacred seal. These pills were swallowed by the patient.

The oldest Anglo-Saxon medical document available to us is called the *Leech Book of Bald*, written for a physician named Bald by a scribe who called himself Cild. This manuscript details a number of leechdoms. In treating a person suffering from headache, the Leech was advised to take "the lower part of the crosswart and put it on a red fillet and bind it around the forehead." Other leechdoms are described in ancient medical writings. "To remove ugly marks from the face, smear with wolf's blood, for it taketh away all marks. For griping also, let the sick drink hound's blood, for it healeth wonderfully."

The ancient Jews treated headache with blood. The Talmud recommended that the pain of a headache could be eased by pouring over the patient's head the blood of a wild rooster killed with a silver coin.

Viking doctors—and the Sagas record that a number of these were women—used the blood of sacrificed animals to speed the healing process. The doctor dipped a finger into the blood and touched it to the injured or ailing part of the body. This form of treatment was known as "Wotan's finger," a name undoubtedly arising from the belief that Wotan was the major god of healing.

Physicians of the Middle Ages used blood to prevent and treat convulsions, epileptic seizures and many other ailments. A medicine made of angelica water, tincture of peony flowers and human blood was widely used in 17th century Europe as a remedy for palsy, asthma, apoplexy and epilepsy. Medical writers of the 16th and 17th centuries devoted considerable attention to the curative powers of blood. Charas, a French physician of the period held that: "All writers extol the volatile salt of man's blood for the cure of epilepsy. It is also effectual in dropsy, in gout and . . . to help eruptions of the skin."

Not all blood was considered effective. "Blood is nature's treasury," wrote Renodaeus; but he warned that: "The blood of a diseased or intemperate man must not be collected and kept in the shops but only that from sound and temperate men."

Red, the color of blood, supposedly had healing powers too—undoubtedly formulated out of the imitative blood magic described earlier. The Old Testament mentions "the water of separation," to be used to purify those who had become contaminated or unclean. The manner in which this purifying wash was to be made is detailed in chapter 19 of the Book of Numbers. A red heifer, without blemish and without even the spot of another color, was to be completely burned—her skin, flesh, blood and dung:

"And the priest shall take cedar wood, and hyssop, and scarlet and cast it into the midst of the burning of the heifer."

The resulting ashes were ceremonially taken to a clean place where they were stored. Whenever purification was required, a small amount of this substance was mixed with clear spring water and sprinkled over the person or article that had to be cleansed of impurity. Thus, the red color of the heifer and the scarlet added to the burning imparted the healing power of blood to this Biblical disinfectant.

With the sanction of Scripture upon it in addition to its other supports, red as a curative color has persisted into modern medicine. We have already noted that many medications are still colored red. Red cheeks and red apples are associated with good health. Red is also a symbol of strength and courage, for instance, in the flag of the United States. In China, much of Asia and many other parts of the world, red denotes health, happiness and good fortune; and anything thus colored is eminently desirable.

The bloodstone, too, was used to treat ailments of the blood or to substitute for blood as a medication for various illnesses. In *The Talisman,* Sir Walter Scott mentioned the healing powers of the bloodstone which ". . . stauncheth blood, driveth away poison, preserveth health; Yea, and some maintain that it provoketh rain and darkeneth the sun, suffering not him that beareth it to be abused."

The phrase "blood bath" evokes many figurative horrors. Yet blood baths were once a literal fact of medical treatment. Pliny reported that the kings of Egypt were bathed in blood as a treatment for leprosy and elephantiasis. Old Hebraic writings elaborate on this: "When the leprous Pharoahs were advised by their astrologers to bathe in human blood, they commanded the slaughter of 150 Jewish children every morning and evening."

The Roman Emperor Constantine, infected with leprosy, was told by his physicians that he could be cured by bathing in the blood of children. Constantine, according to legend, rejected this treatment; instead, he became converted to Christianity and his leprosy was miraculously cured.

Although medicinal blood baths became decreasingly fashionable by the Middle Ages, blood continued to be used in the external treatment of many ailments. Michael Ettmüller, a German physician of the 17th century, held that menstrual blood mixed with crow's fat was a "good application for abscesses and carbuncles."

Blood as a magical medicine even found its way into sympathetic healing. This form of magic was rooted in the belief that illness or pain could be transferred from the patient to some "sympathetic" object; or that a wound or ailment could be cured by treating its cause or some sympathetic substance—such as the patient's blood—even though this might be outside his body. Sympathetic healing was in great vogue in Europe only a few centuries ago and is still in use in some backward parts of the world.

One popular device used in Europe was known as the Sympathetic Egg. A chicken's egg was emptied of its contents and filled with warm blood taken from a healthy human. The egg was then carefully sealed and placed under a brooding hen so that its vitality would not be impaired in any way. At a propitious moment the egg was taken from under the hen and heated for several hours in an oven hot enough to bake bread.

The egg was then ready for its healing task. It was brought to the patient and placed over the affected part of his body. The disease, presumably finding the healthy blood in the egg more attractive than the weakened blood of the patient, entered the egg which was then taken away and buried.

Another form of sympathetic healing, popular throughout Europe in the Middle Ages, was the treatment of wounds by treating the blood that had been spilled. This was still in vogue in England as late as the 17th century. The medicine used was green vitriol and, according to a record of the period: "If a piece of a wounded man's raiment, stained with blood from the wound, were dipped in water holding some of this miraculous powder in solution, the wound of the injured person forthwith began to heal." Time and distance made no difference: "The patient might be dying in Paris or Madrid, and the piece of stained velvet or linen might be operated on in London."

Potent as blood was believed to be, it could become afflicted itself and require treatment. Nosebleed, in which the body spontaneously gave up vital fluid, was held to be a particularly dangerous disease symptom and was treated in many magical ways.

In Europe during the 18th century, nosebleed was treated with various religious charms. One treatment had the person whose nose was bleeding recite aloud the following passage from Ezekial (16:6): "And when I passed by thee, and saw thee polluted in thine own blood, I said unto thee when thou wast in thy blood, Live . . ." Another supposed cure for nosebleed which was in vogue among the British was to have someone write upon the patient's forehead, in the blood flowing from the nose, the final words of Christ according to St. John: "It is finished."

Even today there are people who treat nosebleed by pressing a cold key to the back of the neck or by standing on tiptoe and spitting through a circle made by the thumb and forefinger. Other equally strange folk remedies persist, although their precise origins and the ways in which they are supposed to work have been long forgotten.

Cures for diseased blood and medications to strengthen or enrich blood are almost as old as man himself—and survive in many loudly advertised nostrums.

Charas, the 17th century French physician, believed that vipers, cooked and eaten, were a wonderful medicine and tonic. An unsolicited testimonial to this effect came from Madame de Sévigné who told her son in 1685: "It is to vipers I am indebted for the wonderful health I now enjoy. They temper, purify and refresh the blood."

During this same period, Cornelius Bontekoe of the Netherlands wrote a book in which he advanced the theory that all disease arose from an abnormal thickening of the blood. This grave condition, he asserted, could be corrected by drinking large quantities of tea which would thin the blood. Bontekoe's theory of disease had been held by others before him, but his cure came under sharp attack by his contemporaries who accused him of being in the pay of a group of Dutch tea importers.

Of all the magical cures involving the blood, two were of such importance and attraction that they endured to modern times. One of these, transfusion, has evolved into a well-established scientific procedure. The other, bloodletting, has with a few exceptions passed into the limbo of futility.

To the early witch doctor, transfusion was obviously an eminently reasonable treatment for disease. Since sickness was due to a weakening of the life force within the blood, the addition of healthy blood would strengthen the life force.

The ancient Egyptians, Jews and Syrians practiced blood transfusion, believing that it restored health by restoring the soul.

One of the earliest references to blood transfusion in medicine describes how a Syrian warrior-prince named Naam, was treated for leprosy by a transfusion of blood.

Transfusion was also accepted among the Greeks as a magical restorative. According to Ovid, Medea restored the youth of Pelias by replacing the blood of the aged king with the blood of a ewe which had been fortified with semen and other substances.

The use of animal blood in transfusion remained in practice until relatively modern times. In 1666, Jean Baptiste Denis, the physician of Louis XIV, transfused nine ounces of lamb's blood into a 15-year-old boy who had been almost fatally weakened by an excessive amount of bloodletting in treatment of a fever. The patient improved at first, then died.

Denis continued to practice transfusion, as did some other physicians. Then, following several apparently successful examples of transfusion, the practice came under attack on metaphysical, religious and medical grounds. A violent campaign was leveled against it in France, England, Germany and Italy. It was charged that people transfused with sheep's blood grew wool and horns. The French medical fraternity took a strong stand against it. Finally, a Papal bull was issued forbidding blood transfusion. More than a century passed before doctors returned to a serious study of this procedure.

The magical form of transfusion was practiced until recently by the Zulus. When a Zulu king fell ill, blood was taken from his healthy attendants and mixed with blood from the king. This reinforced blood was then introduced into the king's circulation through a tube to charge it with new strength and healing vigor.

Even after transfusion had been placed on a scientific basis and was beginning to find a place in rational medicine, some rather unusual beliefs persisted. One 19th century German physician suggested, for instance, that temperamentally incompatible couples whose marriages were endangered by quarrels and bickering, could achieve a happier and more harmonious relationship by cross-transfusing their blood.

Unlike transfusion, which evolved out of blood magic to become an important factor in modern medicine despite the opposition of church and state, bloodletting stands as a grotesque monument to man's willingness to accept the dicta of the past without subjecting them to constant scrutiny in the light of unfolding knowledge.

Bloodletting—or phlebotomy—is probably one of the most ancient treatments of disease used by man. According to Pliny man learned about bloodletting from the hippopotamus. The Roman naturalist reported that when a hippopotamus suffered discomfort because of overeating, it would press its body over a sharp reed to break a blood vessel. After enough blood had flowed to ease the animal's discomfort, it would stop the blood by pressing the puncture against limey soil.

To the primitive medicine man, bloodletting was a basic form of healing, for if disease was caused by evil demons in the blood, letting out this infected blood would help free the patient of these demons. Bloodletting was occasionally practiced for moral as well as physical reasons. A woman deemed excessively passionate or flirtatious would be bled to rid her of the love demon. The bleeding was accomplished by opening veins, by using leeches which sucked out the blood, and later by cupping, which drew blood to the body surface.

Bloodletting is another example of man's common response to a common problem. It was practiced by the ancients in Asia and Africa, and by the primitives in Australia, Europe and the Americas. And it has found its way into the mythology of many peoples.

According to Greek mythology, Aesculapius, the Father of Medicine, sired a son named Podalirius who introduced phlebotomy to the world. This son was returning from Troy when a storm wrecked his ship and cast him up upon the coast of Caria. He was rescued by a herdsman who, recognizing Podalirius as a person of importance, took him to the King. The King's daughter, Syrna, had just fallen from the palace roof in a fit and no one seemed able to restore her to consciousness. Podalirius examined the girl and treated her by drawing blood from both her arms. Somehow the girl revived and recovered. Podalirius was given a fortune and, as further reward, received the hand of his royal patient in marriage.

Among the Druids and early Anglo-Saxons, bloodletting was a principal form of healing. The *Leech Book of Bald*, offers the following leechdom for smallpox:

"Against pockes, very much shall one let blood and drink a bowlful of melted butter. . . ." and for paralysis: "Scarify the neck after the setting of the sun, pour in silence the blood into running water. After that, spit three times, then say: 'Have thou this unheal and depart with it . . .' "

Bloodletting became a panacea and was practiced by virtually all doctors, even the greatest of their times. As medical knowledge increased, newer and more elaborate reasons for the practice were devised. Thus bleeding was justified as being able to relieve disease-producing congestion where it was once held to release disease-causing demons.

The untoward effects of bloodletting were probably noted even in early times. After all, removing a pint or so of blood from a sick person did weaken him and make him more susceptible to complicating infections. As a consequence, certain regulations were established to govern bloodletting procedures.

The early Jews were advised that phlebotomy should not be performed more than once in thirty days, and should be decreased with the advancing years of a patient. The most propitious times for bloodletting were supposed to be the first day of the lunar month and the fourteen days before Passover. On the other hand, the month of Ab, when the temple had been destroyed, was considered a most dangerous time for bloodletting.

Among Christians, the Christmas and Easter seasons were considered best for bloodletting. The spirit of peace and good will flourished then and the demons of disease were thought to be at their weakest. But the month of January, when the evil spirits broke loose from the Christmas restraints, was most dangerous for bleeding.

Throughout the Middle Ages, most important churches had a special room put aside where a properly accredited phlebotomist could practice bloodletting under holy auspices. However, mistakes were made even under those regulated circumstances.

The 7th century churchman, John of Beverly once reprimanded a phlebotomist who had bled a patient in an abbey on the fourth day of a month. The patient, instead of improving, took a turn for the worse, causing John to tell the healer: "I remember that Archbishop Theodore, of blessed memory, said that bleeding is very dangerous when both the light of the moon and the flood of the ocean were on the increase."

Bleeding became so widespread that it was taken up by the barber surgeons during the Middle Ages. When the time for bloodletting was propitious, the barbers would notify the public by hanging blood-stained bandages outside their doors. Although barbers no longer practice bloodletting, the red and white striped barber pole remains as a symbol of an earlier practice.

Bleeding also found a place in story and poetry. About 1099, the faculty of the great medieval medical school in Salerno reportedly dedicated a poem to Robert, Duke of Normandy, the son of William the Conqueror. This lengthy poem, entitled *Regimen Sanitatis Salernitanum*, was translated into many languages and contained the following advice:

> The spring is moist, of temper good and warme,
> Then best it is to bathe, to sweate, and purge,
> Then one may ope a veine in either arme,
> If boyling bloud or feare of agues urge:
> Then Venus' recreation doth no harme,
> Yet may too much thereof turne to a scourge.

At the lavish court of Louis XIV, Madame de Maintenon, who was to become the King's consort, had a physician remove several ounces of her blood twice weekly. It seems that she blushed too easily at the purple stories told by the courtiers and their ladies, and hoped that the bleeding would eliminate this sign of naiveté.

Benjamin Rush, America's first accredited physician, was a firm devotee of bleeding. During the great yellow fever epidemic of 1792, Rush bled all the patients who would permit it. The mortality rate was so high, however, that Rush's reputation was severely damaged. Consequently, when George Washington was stricken with his final illness, Rush was ignored and other physicians were called in to treat the first president.

Certainly the treatment Washington received from these doctors was no worse than Rush would have provided. Suffering from a strangling edema of the throat, an ailment which today would be relieved by opening the windpipe, Washington was bled so copiously and repeatedly that his once great strength was exhausted and he died.

There was at least one well-known physician who, like the boy in the fable about the Emperor's new clothes, did not succumb to the age-old self-deception. This was Bernardino Ramazzini, professor at the Universities of Modena and Padua during the 17th century. Credited with being the father of industrial medicine and occupational hygiene, Ramazzini voiced the following opinion of the ancient practice of bleeding: "It seems as if the phlebotomist grasped the Delphic sword in his hand to exterminate the innocent victims rather than to destroy the disease."

Today, after centuries of bloodletting have taken their toll in the name of healing, the practice which arose out of blood magic has been largely discarded. No longer the pervading cure-all, it is now used mainly in special situations where it is necessary to reduce the volume of circulating blood.

Twentieth century man has almost emerged from the caverns of ancient ignorance—but tendrils of darkness still clutch at him. Similarly, knowledge of the blood has slowly evolved from early superstitions and magical concepts.

But the process was so gradual and the division between magic and reason was often so fine, that for thousands of years it was difficult to detect any progress at all. It is only in the last few centuries that we learned that the work of the earliest explorers of the river of life, discarded and long forgotten, provided a more accurate picture than much of what followed.

Part Two THE Early Explorers

Chapter Five The Hunters and the Gods

Blood flowed when a wound was opened. It was red. It did not flow after life was gone. These were probably the first important observations made by those earliest of all explorers of the river of life—the primitive hunters who thus took the first steps to our present level of knowledge.

The early hunter had to be a sharp observer. His environment demanded it. Even today primitive man is more aware of his surroundings than civilized man. This is because his environment provides him with little margin for safety. The African Pygmy must notice the slight disturbance in the pattern of foliage. If he does not, a lurking leopard may kill him. A civilized man may not be aware of the motor car coming at him, but his lack of observation is partly balanced by the fact that the driver of the vehicle will try to avoid running him down. Early man's environment did not offer this measure of protection. So he observed and remembered—or he died.

The remarkable Stone Age paintings in the caverns of the Pyrenees indicate that prehistoric hunters probably knew that a wound to the heart of their quarry was fatal. As practical anatomists, they probably also noticed that a spinal wound brought paralysis and a brain wound usually killed.

Since either the hunters or their women opened the kills, they probably observed the organs—the heart, lungs, liver, stomach, spleen and so on. Of course, they could hardly know the function of all these. But it would have been most unusual if they did not recognize that the stomach was somehow related to digestion since they undoubtedly often found this organ to contain some portion of the animal's last meal.

The liver, because it contained considerable blood, could reasonably be related to the blood. And the heart, which pulsated in life and could even be seen to throb when torn from a wounded animal, must be related to life. It would be obvious that with death the heartbeat stopped, as did the flow of blood.

The hunter probably noticed that wounds in certain parts of the body caused a bright red blood to gush in spurts, while wounds in other parts of the body brought a steady flow of darker blood. It is likely that he also saw the blood vessels of his dead quarry with the veins still holding their congealing blood but with the arteries empty. However, in his observation of the empty arteries he could not have known that with the final pulsations of their muscle-lined walls, these vessels had expelled the blood they contained in life.

All of these observations could have been and probably were made by the primitive hunters. They were knowledge, information, the raw material of science. In some respects it is likely that these early observers had a sounder knowledge of practical anatomy than physicians who lived thousands of years later in eras and cultures that forbade dissection, frowned on research and experimentation.

Although primitive man made certain basic observations which were perfectly correct, he could not, necessarily, interpret them correctly. A relative newcomer to history, he had neither the background, experience nor accumulation of related information to make rational interpretations of many observable phenomena.

He could see that whenever an animal's blood ceased to flow the animal died. But he did not have the knowledge to provide a rational explanation for this event. Instead he decided on a simple and, to him, reasonable interpretation: blood was equal to life and therefore must contain the mysterious essence or substance of life. This gave the blood a supernatural power over life and even death.

Uncounted eons passed between the time the hunter made his first observations regarding the blood and the emergence of the first civilization—when man settled down to till the soil of fertile river valleys. Among the earliest records are those of the land of Sumer, a civilization that flourished about 5,000 years before Christ on the well-watered Mesopotamian plain between the Tigris and Euphrates rivers.

Sumer reached a relatively high state of development before it was overthrown by Akkad, a civilization that was followed by that of Babylon. The Sumerian people emerged out of the Stone Age and learned to use copper and bronze. They developed wheeled carts, mathematics, architecture, scale drawing, writing and even began to chart the heavens.

The medicine of Sumer, like its astrological study of the stars, was essentially magical. The doctors of this ancient land were the priest-conjurers whose knowledge of the blood was hardly greater than that of the early hunter if, indeed, it was not less.

According to the medical tablets that have been found, the Sumerian doctors believed that the blood was a carrier of every vital function and was, in essence, the holder of life itself. How it flowed, they did not know. Nor did they know where it flowed. But they did believe that the liver was the organ that received the blood and, for this reason, was presumed to possess powerful magical qualities. The liver, as the seat of the essential life processes, became an important instrument of divination and prophecy.

The civilization of Mesopotamia passed from Sumer to Akkad and then to Babylon. The physicians of Babylon, who were also its priests, developed the practice of examining the blood of their patients along with their urine. They did this not to determine the nature of the illness—as doctors do today—but to make a magical prophecy of the outcome of the ailment.

The Babylonian priests also observed that there were two kinds of blood—day blood and night blood. Although they could not possibly know this, they were distinguishing between the bright red blood that flowed in the arteries and the darker blood that flowed in the veins.

Despite their early wisdom, the Sumerians and the Babylonians do not seem to have added much to the facts already observed by the primitive hunters. Indeed, they seem to have noted much less since they do not appear to have understood the importance of the heart—something that was evident to Neolithic man, as cave paintings show. Despite their errors and oversights, and the magical framework to which they fitted their observations, the men of Sumer left us a treasure of incalculable importance—a written record of their findings. This was the first deposit in the bank of accumulated human experience.

While Sumerian civilization was developing, nomads from Nubia and East Africa settled and began to grow crops in the rich silt deposited by the annual floods of the Nile River. Other tribes came from Sinai and further east in Asia, found the land fruitful and settled there. Thus the ancient land of Khem—which we know as Egypt—was established.

Egypt was a mixture of peoples who settled in numerous communities and were subjected to a variety of influences, religions and beliefs. From the Orient, according to some anthropologists, came a strong tendency toward mysticism and belief in the supernatural. And from Africa came a sense of pragmatism and day-to-day realism so necessary to survival in the harsh competition of the deserts, plains and forests.

Until a century and a half ago, ancient Egypt was a place of myth and mystery to us. The record was there for us to read but we had no key to the inscriptions. Then, in the early 19th century, a young French Egyptologist named Jean François Champollion deciphered the heiroglyphics of the Rosetta Stone; and the mythical land of Khem assumed the substance of reality. Ancient Egypt, with its incredible store of history and accumulated learning began to unfold before us.

The first Egyptian dynasty was founded about 3,400 years before the Christian era by Menes, known as a physician-king. Even then, as the records indicate, the healing art was held in such high esteem that it was considered a function of kings. The son of Menes, a youth named Atothis who succeeded to the throne of Egypt, was said to have been the author of a book on human anatomy, possibly the first such work in history.

Several hundred years later, in the 32nd century B.C., a book was written, presumably by King Usaphais, dealing with the vessels of the human body. These and other reported works written on papyrus no longer exist. We know of them only because they are referred to in slightly less ancient works that have survived. In any case, these references indicate that rational medicine began in those earliest days of Egypt. Records were kept, studies were made, observations were noted and treatments were charted.

Mysticism and the supernatural could not be entirely avoided. Healing was so important that special gods were designated to control health. The most important of these was Thoth who, according to the legends, cured the god Horus of the venomous sting of a scorpion. As other gods and goddesses became concerned with specific diseases, Thoth finally became associated with diseases of the eye, among the most common of Egyptian ailments.

Following in the footsteps of the gods, the mortal physicians of Egypt also became specialists. Each doctor treated only a particular type of ailment or a special part of the body. One pharaoh had a separate specialist for each of his two eyes. During another early dynasty, specialists who concerned themselves with diseases of the bowel became known as "shepherds of the Rectum."

In the midst of this rapid growth of the healing art in Egypt, an increasing number of observations regarding the blood were made and recorded. One of the most unusual of the surviving early documents is the Ebers Papyrus, which was sold to Georg Ebers in 1873 under rather mysterious circumstances by an Egyptian who apparently had access to a secret store of papyrii from a tomb in Thebes.

The Ebers Papyrus is a perfectly preserved collection of medical documents that had been copied in the year 1553 B.C. by a scribe who was compiling the texts of more ancient times. Egyptologists have since established that this document belonged to the Pharaoh Amenhotep who ruled Egypt in the 16th century before Christ.

It is the Ebers Papyrus that refers to the previously mentioned work of Pharaoh Usaphais, a treatise on the vessels of the human body written some 5,000 years ago. The scribe quotes this document, the earliest record of man's attempt to chart the circulatory system through which flows the river of life:

"Man hath twelve principal vessels proceeding from his heart, which extend to his body and his limbs. Two vessels go to the contents of his chest. Two vessels go to each leg, two to each arm. Two vessels go to the back of the head and from these, two branches go to the eyes and two to the nose. Two branches go to the right ear, through which the breath of life passes; two go to the left ear, through which passes the breath of death."

This belief that associates life to the right side and death to the left side may well be related to the superstition, surviving today, that right-handedness is somehow good and left-handedness is somehow evil.

The Ebers Papyrus also records that it was a function of the vessels to carry air to the systems: ". . . when the breath enters the nostrils it penetrates to the heart and to the internal organs and supplies the body abundantly."

Another achievement recorded in the Ebers Papyrus is the first observation of the pulse. "If the physician places his finger on the neck, head, hands, arms, feet or body, everywhere he will find the heart; for the heart leads to every member and speaks in the vessel of every member."

These observations, dating almost to the beginnings of civilization, were closer to the truth than many beliefs held thousands of years later. They were undoubtedly based on dissection and study. The Egyptian practice of embalming their dead gave them an unusual opportunity to study the interior of the human body and the positions of the organs and vessels. The priests who supervised the Houses of Death where the corpses were prepared believed that the heart was the abode of the soul, the seat of the intellect and that resurrection would be impossible without it. Therefore the heart was not disturbed in the embalming process —but it was closely studied as were the vessels associated with it.

Pharaoh Usaphais was correct in counting twelve principal vessels associated with the heart if not directly connected to it (he included three vessels leading from the aorta rather than from the heart). He could not know, however, that some of these brought blood to the heart and that others carried it away. Nor did he have the means to distinguish between the veins and the arteries. He apparently did not know the function of the lungs, and his description of where the vessels went was accurate only in a most general sense. Nevertheless, as the earliest recorded description of the circulation, this stands as a landmark of human achievement.

In Egypt, the gods became physicians—it remained only for a physician to become a god. About 3,000 B.C., during the reign of Pharaoh Djoser, a man appeared who was probably the world's first true physician. His name was Imhotep.

Apparently Imhotep was a man with a vast store of talents, as was Leonardo da Vinci thousands of years later. He was, like his father before him, an architect—an important profession in a land where the building of tombs was a sacred art. He is said to have designed the Step Pyramid at Sakkara as a tomb for Pharaoh Djoser. This structure, believed to be Egypt's oldest pyramid, still stands today.

Imhotep was Djoser's Grand Vizier, a priest and a scribe. He conducted the sacred rituals for his king, and was noted as an astronomer. When the failure of the Nile to overflow its banks brought drought and hunger to Egypt for seven years, Imhotep is said to have prevailed upon Chnum, the ram-headed God of the Cataracts, to release the floods.

Most important of all, Imhotep was a physician. Although legend surrounds him with miracles, he was fundamentally a rational physician who left the first priceless record of case histories. Imhotep's work, mentioned in other papyrii and remembered in legend as *The Secret Book of the Physician,* was long believed to be a myth. Then, in 1862, an American named Edwin Smith managed to obtain a papyrus which had been written about 1,700 B.C.

There were some strange aspects to the Smith Papyrus. First of all, it was one of the most important medical documents to come down from ancient times. Despite this, no mention of such an original work had been found in any of the references to the period in which it was presumably written.

For many years, the Smith Papyrus was subjected to close scrutiny and it was at last determined that it was not an original work at all but the copy of a manuscript written at least a thousand years before 1,700 B.C. Finally the great Egyptologist, James H. Breasted, came forward with the suggestion that the Smith Papyrus was the copy of a work originally written by Imhotep, and may indeed be *The Secret Book of the Physician.*

This papyrus, which Breasted hailed as "a fascinating revelation of the human mind struggling with the first stages of science building," reports in carefully organized fashion, 48 cases involving wounds and surgery. Each case begins with a detailed description of the ailment. Then there is a report of the examination and an account of the symptoms observed. This is followed by an extensive diagnosis and a flat statement as to whether or not the ailment could be treated. Then, where treatment was held possible, there is given an account of the proposed therapy.

Many of the observations in this ancient text are so accurate and precisely detailed that they might have been written by a modern physician. The brain is described for the first time with an indication that it was recognized as the site of the mental functions. The effects of spinal injuries on the functions of the intestines and bladder are clearly noted. Only once in the entire manuscript is the use of magic mentioned. With this single exception, it is as objective a work of science as mankind has yet produced.

In this papyrus, which certainly fits the description of the work by Imhotep, an understanding of the circulation and the role of the blood is implicit. Some scholars believe that Imhotep may have provided the first accurate description of the circulation, although this is by no means proved. Certainly he did have considerable knowledge of the blood, and this was used in the healing that he practiced. Even more to Imhotep's credit was his clear, organized approach to a subject which was soon to be inundated by a swell of superstition and tradition.

Imhotep's medical fame grew so great that by the time he died he was revered as a kind of healing saint. He was buried at Memphis and, ironically, the sick began to make pilgrimages to his tomb in order that they be miraculously healed. Shrines were dedicated to him and later a temple was erected in his name. Finally, in the year 525 B.C., when Egypt had fallen to Persian conquest, Imhotep—already a demigod—was elevated to full godhood and became the Patron Diety of Medicine, "Under whose protection life is dealt to all men and who gives a son to him who has none."

His biography was changed. No longer was he the son of mortal parents. He was honored as the first-born of the gods Ptah and Sekhmet, able to cure the sick, make barren women fertile and bring happiness to the unfortunate.

Two centuries later, when Egypt was ruled by the Macedonian Ptolemies, a shrine was built to Imhotep on the island of Philae where festivals were held every two months to commemorate important events in his mythical life. Part of this shrine still stands. The worship of Imhotep became so widespread that the Greeks merged him with their own God of Healing, Aesculapius; and the temple at Memphis was devoted to the worship of a new, amalgamated deity, *Imuthes-Asklepios.*

Imhotep's conversion from rational healer to superstition-shrouded deity paralleled what happened to Egyptian medicine during that same period. In the thousands of years after the period of the Old Kingdom, Egypt grew in the greatness of her conquests, in the number and power of her gods and in the multitudes of her slaves. But in the practice of healing and in the study of the human body, Egypt became imprisoned in traditionalism and, after 1,600 B.C., declined into sorcery. Imhotep, Usaphais and Athotis were never again matched.

On the other side of Asia, the Hwang-ho, the Yangtse and the Si Kiang Rivers nurtured another great civilization—China. There, as in Egypt, the earliest days were marked by a great drive to answer the most practical needs in the most practical way. This was the pragmatic empiricism of primitive times—the practice of separating the useful from the useless through the reality of trial and error.

In China as in Egypt, beliefs arising out of magic and superstition hardened into a religious view of the cosmos into which all truths had to fit. According to this philosophy, all things were believed to arise out of the opposition of the two principles—the Yang and Yin—which, in their opposition, formed the totality of any reality. The Yang was masculine, the Yin was feminine.

The Yang represented heaven, the sun, all of the active, positive qualities. The Yin represented the earth, darkness, all the passive, negative qualities. Out of the perfect equilibrium of these two principles arose health, wisdom, happiness, tranquility, peace and all that was good and desirable. Out of a disturbance of this equilibrium came disease, folly, war and all that was evil.

All of China's medicine and science, especially after the 11th century A.D., had to fit into the formula of Yang and Yin. Nevertheless, before these beliefs became inflexible, some of the early Chinese physicians made a number of important observations which were handed down to be copied and recopied as part of the ancient wisdom.

According to legend, Chinese medicine originated with the Emperor Shen Nung who is said to have lived about 2,700 B.C. One of the oldest medical works in existence is the *Nei Ching*, or *The Book of Medicine*, purportedly written some time prior to 2,600 B.C. by the Emperor Hwang-ti. It is in this ancient work, still studied today, that we find an observation regarding the river of life so extraordinarily advanced that it anticipated Harvey's monumental work on the circulation by more than 42 centuries.

"All the blood is under the control of the heart," wrote the legendary Hwang-ti. "The heart regulates all the blood of the body. The blood current flows continuously in a circle and never stops. It may be compared to a circle without beginning and without end."

Although generalized, this was the first accurate statement of the circulation. The nature of the blood, its composition and its function was described by another Chinese physician: "The blood is the fluid tissue of the body. It is formed from the solid and liquid foods which are eaten and enter the belly where the food is transformed. In the abdomen the blood becomes red and passes to the various vessels, nourishing the whole body and transporting the vital principles."

Thus, thousands of years ago, man perceived truths that we

have only recently rediscovered. The blood was recognized as a fluid tissue, which it is. There was the awakening of an understanding of nutrition and metabolism. The role of the blood as a transport vehicle had been noted. And the circulatory course of the blood, driven by the heart, was postulated.

Unfortunately, these discoveries were made too early. Man had neither the background nor the knowledge to understand them or utilize them correctly. Here we meet one of history's less gentle ironies: for man to be able to use a discovery, his society, his science and his technology must be ready for it.

A bacterial theory of illness would have been nonsense to Hippocrates because, for one thing, microscopes to make bacteria visible did not exist in his time. Automation and similar labor-saving machines would have been impractical in Egypt because slave labor was cheaper and required less maintenance.

The very early explorers charted a number of fundamental truths about the river of life, and came close to others. But human society was not yet ready. However, there was one correct observation which, incorrectly interpreted, wielded a great influence over thousands of years. The early Egyptians, the Chinese and even the great physician of ancient India, Susruta, all noted that certain vessels leading from the heart were empty. These vessels were the arteries and the observation regarding them was valid since, at death, the muscular pulse of the artery walls expells the blood into the capillaries and veins.

Not knowing that the arteries, though empty at death, carried blood during life, the ancients assumed that these vessels carried air or some vital spirit. In a world in which life was a supernatural rather than a natural phenomenon, this was a perfectly reasonable and acceptable assumption. From it arose the belief that through our arteries flowed the vital spirit or soul—a concept that for many thousands of years was to distort man's understanding of the circulation.

Chapter Six

The Metaphysical Physicians

At about the time an Egyptian scribe copied certain ancient texts into what we know as the Ebers Papyrus, successive waves of nomadic tribes were beginning to push down into the Balkan peninsula and Asia Minor in a hunt for richer land and better pastures. With restless vigor and armed with iron weapons, these semi-barbarians came out of Eastern Europe and the steppes north of the Caspian Sea to engulf the civilizations in their path—the Aegean, Minoan and that mysterious culture of what is now Turkish Anatolia.

First came the Ionian tribes, then Aeolian, Dorian, Thracian, Macedonian and other peoples who, sharing a similar tongue and background, were known as the Hellenes, or Greeks. They absorbed what they conquered, added to it and then, in a stupendous outburst of human creativity, carried civilization to new heights.

After they took over the great maritime culture of Crete and the Aegean islands, they spread out into Asia Minor, planting settlements along the Black Sea. They moved into North Africa, eastward to Sicily, to southern Italy and at least as far as southern France where they founded a community which later became Marseilles.

Individualism was a characteristic of Greek society. Not only were the colonies widely scattered but in Greece the rugged nature of the mountainous land separated the cities, just as the Aegean waters separated the many settled islands. Consequently, although the individualistic Greek tribesmen retained their unity of language and a basically common culture, their communities were at first largely autonomous and independent.

Out of this spirit of freedom, probably retained from earlier nomadic times, arose the influences that made Greek thought and art so fruitful in the early stages of Hellenic history.

Fortunately for Western civilization, religion in Greece did not become a dominating factor; a rigid, priestly caste able to exercise power and authority never developed. The Greeks believed in their gods and myths, but more as a matter of poetry and aesthetics than as instruments of dogma and control. Fear of supernatural punishment did not fetter the early Greeks. So they were free to develop ideas, to believe or disbelieve, to question and to dispute. Greek thought, unchained, could soar to explore the complex meanings of the universe.

Greek society was a vigorous democracy as far as its own citizens were concerned. But it also used, on an increasing scale, the labor of slaves. Free Greek artisans, farmers and laborers, forced to compete with slaves, were gradually degraded, as was the very concept of labor. This had a powerful effect on the philosophy and science of the Greeks as well as on their exploration of the blood.

As the Greek social order became more rigid, certain attitudes developed among Greek thinkers. Since labor was the lot of the slave or artisan, it became degrading for a cultured person to perform physical work or do anything with his hands. It was considered more suitable to range the vast realms of pure thought. The Greek was freed from the need for work and could, instead, dispute, debate or link a progression of ideas into a great philosophical concept of the universe.

Thoughts became more important than things, abstractions more important than realities, the products of metaphysical reasoning more important than the products of physical labor. If an experiment which required labor contradicted an accepted metaphysical concept, the experiment was more likely to be considered at fault. These attitudes did not prevail throughout Greek history, but they were sufficiently pervasive to withhold from Greek science and technology much of the scope that was allowed to her philosophy.

In order to understand the blood and chart its course, it is necessary to study the physical structure of man as well as the nature and function of his organs—his anatomy and physiology. The Greek philosophers felt they were above this sort of study because it required physical labor. They deemed the physiology of man less important than the metaphysical concepts of the nature of man and his place in the universe. So the physical studies were left to the physicians, inferior to philosophers because they worked with their hands. And where the physician's finding about the physical structure of man's body conflicted with the philosopher's metaphysical concept of man, the philosopher usually prevailed.

Greece's earliest record of investigation of blood comes to us through Homer who, since no other writing of that period survives, serves as a historian as well as poet and mythologist. Most of what we know of early Greek history, culture and manners comes to us from the *Iliad* and *Odyssey*.

From Homer we can see that the anatomical knowledge of the early Greeks was very primitive. Since people who died a natural death stopped breathing but did not lose blood, it was believed that in those cases the life essence escaped with the breath. But where a person died of a wound, the life essence escaped with the outflowing blood.

In the *Iliad*, Homer describes about 140 wounds and tells how a number of them were treated; for example, the flow of blood was stopped by the use of compresses and bandages. Homer even shows that the beating of the heart was known. When the Trojan warrior Alcathous had a spear driven into him by Idomeneus, he "fell to earth with noise; the spear stood firmly planted in his heart and, as he panted, it quivered through its length."

The physicians of the Homeric days were not priests but laymen who, by trial and error, had developed a healing art. And the semi-mythical Greek heroes, great warriors skilled in deeds of violence, were also healers. One of the finest pieces of Greek art, a vase by the artist Sosias, shows Achilles treating the wounded arm of his friend Patroclus.

After the period described by Homer, expanding Hellenic civilization absorbed some of the oriental influences with which it came into contact. From Egypt and further East came growing mystical influence and, as the poetic Greek religion became more formal and distinct, their gods became healers in much the same way as had the gods of Egypt thousands of years before.

Apollo became the inventor of the healing art. Athene, and even Zeus himself, became known as healers. But the Greeks selected none of these pure divinities to become their god of medicine. Instead they invented one with a touch of everyday humanity.

They mated the Sun god, Apollo, with a pretty young maiden of Thessaly—a girl known as Coronis. Out of this union a son was born, the demi-god Aesculapius. As befitted young men of prominent lineage, Aesculapius was turned over to the centaur Chiron. In Chiron's cave on Mount Pelion, a school where such heroes as Jason, Hercules and Achilles studied the arts in which they were to excel, Aesculapius learned the art of healing. The legends tell us that Aesculapius' healing powers grew so vast that he could cure all ills, restore wasted limbs and even return the dead to life. This finally enraged Zeus who believed that the power of life and death belonged to him alone. In his Olympian anger he loosed a thunderbolt at Aesculapius and slew him.

Aesculapius, assisted by two of his mythological daughters, Hygiea, the goddess of health, and Panacea, goddess of all-healing herbs, was worshipped by the Greeks as the supreme god of medicine. A cult of healing grew around him, with numerous sanctuaries and shrines where the sick came for miraculous cures. The priest who supervised these centers of healing "miracles" practiced rational economics if not rational medicine. They demanded and received payment for their treatments. Theoretically, patients were supposed to leave "thank offerings" based on ability to pay before treatment was begun, but these were more compulsory than voluntary. The Aesculapian priests were so astute financially that, according to some historians, they worked out a system of time payments for those who were unable to pay all at once. The contracts were never drawn for a period longer than one year.

While the Aesculapian shrines attracted many followers, this priestly form of healing never became powerful enough to block the growth of a more rational form of medicine. Greek thinkers rejected magic and dogma and tried to apply what they considered purely logical methods to explain natural phenomena. From these explanations they then sought to evolve generalizations that could embrace the cosmos. Great lovers of beauty, they believed that truth existed in harmony, order and balance. Out of these metaphysical concepts flowed the art, science and medicine of Greece.

During the flowering of Greek culture, one of the earliest investigators of the blood was Alcmaeon of Croton (a city in southern Italy) who lived about 500 B.C. Fragments of his book *On Nature* are said to have been preserved in the works of later writers. A considerable portion of the medical writings of the great physician Hippocrates may also have been derived from Alcmaeon's earlier teachings.

From the little that is known of Alcmaeon, he evidently believed in close and critical investigation and was the first to dissect animals for anatomical study. This was a major development in scientific history for, though similar discoveries had been made earlier by the Egyptians and Chinese, it led to a number of notable anatomical discoveries in the West.

Alcmaeon found, for instance, that veins and arteries were different forms of vessels. He also concluded that the movement of the blood, while it might not always be uniform, was continuous. This was a revolutionary statement for the time since it implied that the blood circulated through the system. Unfortunately, neither Greek knowledge nor science were able to seize upon this implication and carry it further.

Alcmaeon believed that health consisted of the equilibrium of all the elements of the body. Disease resulted when the harmony was disturbed. To cure an ailment it thus became necessary to remove the disturbance and restore the harmonious balance.

Once again we see an example of widely separated peoples independently arriving at similar conclusions. Alcmaeon's theory of disease, arising from the application of Greek metaphysics to medical observations, was virtually identical to the Chinese theory of disease based on the philosophical principles of Yang and Yin.

The blood was a vitally important factor in the regulation of the body, according to Alcmaeon. He also recognized the brain as the center of the intellect, of movement and of the senses—another advanced observation for his time. Alcmaeon believed that any movement of blood away from the brain caused disturbances in its function. Sleep and even death, he taught, were caused by the transfer of blood away from the brain and into the vessels.

We now know that his theory of sleep is incorrect, yet it indicates that Alcmaeon made some astonishingly astute observations during the course of his animal dissections. Unconsciousness, which may appear like normal sleep, often is associated with a reduced flow of blood to the brain. And even in sleep, although the total blood flow does not vary appreciably from wakefulness, there may be a diminished flow to the brain areas concerned with waking activities. Clearly, Alcmaeon had much to offer toward a fuller understanding of the blood.

At the same time Alcmaeon flourished in Croton, another Greek philosopher-physician, Empedocles, advanced some interesting theories in his native city of Agrigentum on the island of Sicily. As a philosopher, Empedocles taught that all things, including the human body, were composed of the four elements—earth, water, fire and air—in differing proportions. Two influences acted upon all the elements of the universe, he said. These forces were the opposing principles of concord and discord, love and hate. Here, too, we see a similarity to Yang and Yin.

In his search for philosophic harmony, Empedocles made a number of observations regarding the blood and its flow. While these were not necessarily correct, they were important because of the influence they had upon other thinkers.

"Blood is life," declared Empedocles, "the seat of intellect and perception, and the innate source of human heat." He also taught that blood carried the essence of physical animation and, obviously, he disputed Alcmaeon's contention that the brain was the seat of the intellect and the senses. Sweat and tears, he held, were thinner parts of the blood.

Although Empedocles is remembered mainly for his sweeping philosophical concepts, some of his practical achievements are worthy of note. When the Sicilian city of Salinus was periodically beset by an unknown pestilence—which may have been malaria —Empedocles was called upon to help. Apparently realizing that the swamps and marshes surrounding the city were a factor in the epidemic, he ordered them drained. The citizens of Salinus were so grateful at the defeat of the pestilence, that they struck gold coins to honor their benefactor.

As Greek civilization grew and its philosophers explored and disputed the expanding reaches of thought, distinct schools of medicine appeared in scattered parts of Greece. They arose out of particular philosophic doctrines rather than medical findings. One formed in southern Italy around the philosophy of Pythagoras and another in Sicily around the doctrines of Empedocles. Other important schools flourished in Cyrene, on the islands of Cos and Rhodes, and in Cnidus, a Greek colony in what is now Asian Turkey. Each of these schools, using different metaphysical concepts in their approach to healing, affected the study of the blood.

The school at Cnidus, although strongly influenced by the Egyptians at the outset, knew very little anatomy. Yet one of its outstanding physicians, Euryphon—who wrote a book called

Livid Liver—was one of the few men of his time who took the trouble to observe that the arteries of living creatures did contain blood. He had noted that when an artery was cut, it bled. From this observation he drew the obvious conclusion—that while the arteries of the dead were empty, the arteries of the living could hold blood. This experimental fact happened to contradict the prevailing concept accepted by the metaphysicians, that the life essence, or pneuma, flowed through the arteries. So, an elaborate rationalization was developed which held that the arteries contained only pneuma; and a *cut* artery drew blood from the surrounding veins, the blood flowing out with the pneuma.

Like so many other of man's early discoveries, Euryphon's scientifically accurate observation was molded to fit a false prevailing concept and thus lost to the realm of reason.

The school at Cos gave to the Western world one of its greatest physicians, a man who has had a profound influence on healing right to the present day. Hippocrates, whose observations of a patient were as detailed as those of Imhotep, provided medicine with a vast body of literature, a code of ethics embodied in the Hippocratic Oath still taken by physicians, and a highly rational approach to healing. At the same time, influenced by the metaphysicians, he produced a humoural theory of disease that was to retard man's understanding of illness for two thousand years.

The facts of Hippocrates' life are shrouded in fancy, myth and dispute. He was presumably born on Cos about 460 B.C. He lived to an advanced age, perhaps 95 years or possibly even 104 years. His father was the physician Heracleides, under whom he studied.

Until the Middle Ages, Hippocrates was generally regarded as the father of medicine and one of the greatest physicians of ancient times, if not of all time—at least among Westerners. Since each culture assumes that its traditions are universal, we should recognize that the Egyptians might favor Imhotep, the Indians might be inclined toward Susruta and the Chinese might choose the Emperor Hwang-ti.

Hippocrates won reverence despite the fact that he had only a scanty knowledge of anatomy and physiology. He could not even distinguish between a vein and artery. His record of cures was hardly remarkable. Of the 42 cases so carefully reported in the writings attributed to him, 25 ended with the death of the patient.

What gave lustre to Hippocrates' reputation was the fact that he had one of the most probing minds of his time. He believed that everything was subject to natural laws. Disease, he taught, was not divinely inspired or haphazardly inflicted. It arose out of specific, natural causes. Furthermore, he believed that disease affected the whole patient and not just a particular part of him. Therefore, the physician had to treat the patient as a whole. Plato stated the Hippocratic approach in these words: "To heal even an eye one must heal the head and, indeed, the whole body."

In keeping with this view of healing, Hippocrates emphasized direct observation of the afflicted part, of the patient and even of the environment in which the patient lived. Since disease was a natural process to which the body reacted, it was the task of the physician to help the body cure itself.

This approach was far ahead of the contemporary theories of healing and it marked an epochal advance. Then, as so many other brilliant men have done before and since, Hippocrates brought forth an equally stunning absurdity. This was his attempt to describe the causes and mechanisms of the disease process in terms of the accepted philosophic "truths" of his time.

Disease was a natural process, according to Hippocrates. But he defined nature in metaphysical rather than natural terms. Since he believed that all nature was composed of the four elements—earth, water, fire and air—he reasoned that the body contained four fluids, or humours, related to these elements.

The black bile, cold and dry, was related to the element earth.

The phlegm, cold and moist, was related to water.

The blood, hot and moist, was related to air.

The yellow bile, hot and dry, was related to fire.

When these four humours were in perfect balance, a person enjoyed perfect health. An imbalance produced illness. To treat an ailment, a physician had to determine the nature of the imbalance and seek to correct it. In this way, if a physician decided that an ailment was due to an excess of black bile, which was cold and dry, he might try to treat it by stimulating the blood which was hot and moist.

This theory of disease, again remarkably similar to the theory developed earlier by the Chinese, gained such support that it survived almost to modern times. Here we have another of history's quaint ironies—that which was rational and scientific in the Hippocratic approach was largely ignored, while the metaphysical theory of the humours was seized upon with religious devotion. Apparently the mystical, the supernatural and the metaphysical have an attraction for man not shared by the less voluptuous disciplines of reason and science.

With all of his fallacies, Hippocrates injected into his humoural theory an idea which struck close to a profound fact about the blood, one we have learned only in comparatively recent times. This was his contention that the humours contained in the blood produced more profound effects than those in any single organ. Furthermore, he said, "The glands have the purpose of providing for the distribution of the humours in the body," anticipating the discovery of the functions of the endocrine glands as well as the role of the blood as a carrier of hormones for the regulation of body processes.

It is mankind's loss that the Greece of Hippocrates valued labor less than thought, the physical less than the metaphysical and experimental facts less than abstract concepts. The doctors of Greece, her scientists, all who conducted experiments which involved physical activity or labor, were considered artisans or craftsmen. Physicians ranked below jewelers but above cobblers in the social scale. A vestige of this class distinction still exists among the British where a surgeon, who must work with his hands, is called "Mister" while the physician, whose work is more cerebral, is referred to as "Doctor."

The philosophical aspects of Athenian creativity also suffered from this early scorn for the labor of experiment. Had the daring Greek thinkers allowed themselves to test their theories thoroughly and relate them more closely to observable and measurable phenomena, their achievements might have been truly Olympian.

Instead, Plato explored the ideal essences of things and concluded that the blood vessels originated from the heart which was the seat of the mind. Through these vessels the mind was thus able to receive the commands of its superior, the soul.

Aristotle, torn between abstract philosophy and experimental realism, observed nature and conducted some experiments. But he tended to color his conclusions with metaphysics. He believed in the pneuma or vital spirit, and that the arteries somehow served to convey motion to the limbs. He believed that the blood flowed out from the heart in an inexhaustible stream that never returned —apparently vanishing somewhere into the system.

Aristotle also held the brain to be a mass of earth and water, without blood or sensation, the function of which was to maintain the heat balance of the heart. And he thought the pulse was caused by the bubbling of vital heat in the blood.

Thus, in the classical Greek period which saw such a monumental outburst of human creativity, the knowledge of the blood and circulation increased only slightly and never really approached that level attained by the earlier Egyptians and Chinese.

The Greek genius, free and soaring in its vaster concepts, exhausted itself in metaphysical abstractions just as other cultures were immobilized by mysticism and the supernatural. But Hippocrates and the other explorers built a great potential for discovery which broke loose after Athens was toppled by the vigor that exploded out of Macedon.

Chapter Seven

The Giants of Alexandria

As they swept through Egypt, across Asia Minor and deep into the Asian heartland, the armies of Alexander the Great carried more than the shattering impact of Macedonian fighting power. At least as potent, and certainly more enduring, were the ideas that they brought. These spread outward from the advancing armies like a tidal wave, sweeping away the barriers of intellectual separateness and cultural isolation.

People in the Mediterranean basin, the valley of the Indus and even the bleak uplands of Central Asia, suddenly discovered that each man was a part of a larger mankind and began to share their hoarded stores of knowledge and experience.

Just as the culture of the Greeks influenced the nations that came under their sway, the Greeks in turn came into contact with new philosophies and ways of life. The cross-fertilization of ideas in this interchange produced fruit long after the dust of Alexander's empire was scattered by the winds of history.

The Alexandrian conquests resembled those clashes of cultures that came some 15 centuries later—the Crusades, which produced the leavening of ideas that helped lead Europe out of the Dark Ages and toward the Renaissance.

Deep changes took place in Greece under the spur of Alexander and the Macedonians. There was a release of new energy and restlessness. Creative drives were poured into active rather than contemplative pathways. The schools of abstract philosophers became more moral and spiritual and lost much of their influence on scientific thought. The art, literature and politics of Greece became relatively static. But in the natural sciences, in mathematics, astronomy, mechanics and anatomy, there was an explosion of fresh activity which seemed to increase when Alexander's empire fell apart following his death in 323 B.C.

The major portions of the empire were taken over by Alexander's Macedonian generals. Persia fell into the hands of Seleucus, who founded the Seleucid dynasty. Egypt went to Ptolemy, an unusually gifted individual with political skill and extraordinary intellectual attainments.

In his capital city of Alexandria, Ptolemy I set up the Museum, an establishment dedicated to the Muses. A state-supported institution, it offered the opportunity to engage in study, research, writing and teaching. Some of the most brilliant men of the time were attracted to the Museum, and ideas and the reports of experiments were forwarded to the Museum from scientists in other parts of the classical world.

Along with the Museum, a great library was founded to gather all the available writings of the world, translate them into Greek and place them at the disposal of the scholars. Thus, Alexandria became the repository of mankind's recorded wisdom, and, for a brief period, the fountainhead of some of man's proudest intellectual achievements.

The Alexandrian scientists, released from the metaphysical restraints of the philosophers, tested their assumptions by experiment. As a result, the science of Alexandria bounded forward at an incredible rate and reached a level that was not touched again for almost two thousand years. Among the great Alexandrian teachers and students were Euclid, who organized the structure of geometry, Eratosthenes, who measured the diameter of the earth with an error of only 50 miles, Hipparchus, who mapped and catalogued the stars, Hero, who made the first steam engine, and Archimedes who laid the foundations of mechanics and who, according to legend, believed that with a fulcrum and a lever long enough he could move the earth.

The first of the Alexandrian explorers of the river of life was

Herophilus, said to be a grandson of Aristotle. He was born about 330 B.C. in Chalcedon, a city of Bithynia in Asia Minor and studied medicine at Cos, the stronghold of the Hippocratic school.

His teacher at Cos was the noted anatomist Praxagoras who had once dissected a corpse and noted the difference between the veins and arteries. Herophilus was a brilliant student. Drawn by the intellectual and experimental freedom allowed to scientists by Ptolemy, he came to Alexandria where he soon established a reputation as one of the great anatomists of his time.

Herophilus enjoyed an advantage permitted few investigators prior to the Alexandrian period. He was able to dissect the human body. This had been and was still taboo to most other peoples of the world including the Greeks. Even the great Aristotle had drawn his conclusions regarding human anatomy from the study of animals. Herophilus believed that the human body was unique and, while it might be similar to that of a lower animal in some respects, it had many characteristics that were exclusively human. Therefore, to learn the human body it was essential to study it.

Ptolemy agreed, and ordered that the corpses of criminals be turned over to Herophilus for dissection and study. Egypt still practiced embalming and the cutting open of cadavers was an established part of the procedure. But dissection was viewed with revulsion elsewhere. Scandalous stories were spread to discredit Herophilus, Ptolemy and anyone else who practiced, endorsed or contemplated dissection. More than 600 years later, in the second century of the Christian era, a story accused Herophilus of actually cutting open the bodies of 600 living criminals while Ptolemy looked on with sadistic pleasure. The distinguished anatomist was even referred to as "Herophilus the Butcher."

Despite later distortions, the work of Herophilus stands as a landmark in man's long groping toward knowledge of his physical nature. Among his important findings was the recognition of the true nature of the nerves. Earlier Greeks had imagined the nerves to be some sort of blood vessels; but Herophilus showed them to be part of a system, including the brain and spinal column, which transmitted sensations and determined movements. He saw the brain as the center of intelligence and the nervous system, and provided anatomical evidence to contradict the metaphysical conclusions of Plato and Aristotle that the heart was the seat of the intellect.

Herophilus's attempts to unravel the nature of the blood and its circulation were generally in vain, yet he did succeed in making an important contribution. This was his discovery of the pulse—which the earlier Chinese and Egyptians had recognized—and its use in the diagnosis of disease.

He viewed the pulse as a phenomenon that took place in the blood vessels, and tried to analyze these pulsations as the vessels contracted and dilated. Using a water clock to count the pulse rate under varying conditions, he combined this information with such other factors as the strength and rhythm of the pulse in order to determine the state of the body's health.

The varying rhythms of the pulse fascinated him. He classified them and gave them special names. One of these, "the goat-leap" pulse, is still in use. Unfortunately, Herophilus then went off on a strange tangent which led nowhere.

Since rhythm was related to music, he assumed that theories of musical order and harmony could be applied to the pulse in order to determine the conditions affecting the body. Out of this vaguely mystical approach a doctrine of the pulse evolved that was so intricate only a doctor who was also a trained musician could understand it.

Despite his great skill, vigorous imagination and the freedom to experiment afforded by Ptolemy, Herophilus never broke his links to the Hippocratic school in which he had been trained. He accepted the theory of the four humours and even believed that a portion of the heart contained the soul.

It remained for Erasistratus, who came a generation after Herophilus, to reject the bland acceptance of tradition, and fulfill a large portion of the promise of the Alexandrian period. A most unusual individual in many ways, Erasistratus developed an approach to medicine that, had it been accepted, might have speeded man's achievements in the conquest of disease by more than a thousand years.

Born on the island of Chios about 310 B.C., Erasistratus grew up in the city of Antioch, capital of the Seleucid Empire that had been carved out of Alexander's vast but ephemeral domain. He studied at many schools and under many teachers, learning the theories of Aristotle, of Hippocrates and the others. Then, to round out his training, he completed his formal studies at the Cnidian school where he received his most important influences.

When he came to Alexandria, Erasistratus was already a man of broad training and experience. Having delved into the conflicting theories of healing that flourished—and knowing how fanatically each was supported—he understood that tradition did not necessarily guarantee truth. So, traditional or not, he rejected those theories he could neither believe nor confirm. Among these was the humoural doctrine of disease promulgated by Hippocrates. As far as was possible for his time, he tried to submit each theory and belief to the tests of observation and experiment.

Superstition, war and ignorance obliterated the records of most of the work done by Erasistratus and the other great Alexandrians. Only a fraction of it survived, mainly in the writings of others. But from these fragments we can estimate the wealth of Erasistratus's total contribution. To call it vast would be an understatement.

Free to experiment and to dissect the organs of cadavers, Erasistratus gave us the most complete and nearly accurate description of the circulation that had been achieved by Western man until that time. He recognized that the heart was a pump, comparing it to a blacksmith's bellows. He described its appearance and discovered that it possessed valves which permitted the blood to flow only in a single direction.

Erasistratus believed that the blood was formed in the liver.

This was an understandable conclusion since the liver does help form blood in human and most animal embryos, but loses this ability shortly before birth when the blood-forming function is taken over by the bone marrow and the lymph gland tissues.

He correctly traced the blood from the liver to the right side of the heart which it entered by way of the great vein known as the *inferior vena cava.* From the right side of the heart he traced the blood through the pulmonary arteries to the lungs. Here, again, Erasistratus proved remarkably accurate.

Then he fell into an unfortunate error—one of interpretation rather than of observation. The error, of course, was the old one about the arteries being empty of blood. Working on cadavers and charting the course of the blood with extreme care, he found the arteries to be empty and drew the obvious but incorrect conclusion that they contained pneuma instead of blood. Consequently, while his picture of the vessels leading back from the lungs to the left side of the heart and then out into the body was a gem of accuracy, he failed to realize that these too carried blood.

Thus, while he provided a nearly perfect general map of the circulation, he mistakenly believed it to be two systems rather than one. The blood, prepared in the liver, was pumped through the veins by the right side of the heart. The air, or pneuma, breathed into the lungs was pumped through the arteries by the left side of the heart.

Since blood was seen to flow from the cut arteries of living creatures, Erasistratus deduced that there were tiny vessels connecting the veins to the arteries. This closely reasoned anticipation of the capillary system which leads from the arteries to the veins ranks high in the achievements of the human intellect. Had William Harvey either known of or grasped the implications of this work when he mapped the circulation some 2,000 years later, he would have been able to arrive at a clearer understanding of how the arterial blood finally entered the veins.

Erasistratus was also a great innovator in the practice of medicine. We have seen that he spurned the prevailing Hippocratic doctrine of the four humours. He believed instead that illness was related to changes in the tissues and organs of the body. He studied the differences between healthy and diseased organs, noted the pathological changes and attempted to evolve a theory of disease that took these factors into account. Had this theory been explored further instead of the Hippocratic doctrine, medicine might have progressed much more rapidly.

Erasistratus's reputation as a physician spread to three continents during his lifetime and gave rise to a number of legends. One of the best known of these stories was related by Plutarch and even inspired a number of paintings.

Seleucus Nicator, the Macedonian general who founded the Seleucid Dynasty in Syria, had a son named Antiochus who was to inherit the throne. Antiochus, a vigorous young man, fell in love with a beautiful young lady named Stratonice, who, unfortunately, had recently become one of his step-mothers. Seleucus, already an old man, had taken the lovely Stratonice into his harem, probably for political rather than sentimental or dynastic reasons. But the Crown Prince was much too honorable a young man to express his love or even reveal it to anyone. In his attempts to suppress his intense but secret passion, he withdrew from his friends and activities, grew melancholy and ceased to care for his appearance or tend to his normal wants.

The king, disturbed by the strange and mysterious illness that was destroying his son, called in physician after physician. They accomplished nothing and could not even diagnose the ailment. Finally Seleucus called the renowned Erasistratus.

The physician came to the Selucid court and studied the melancholy prince closely. After several days of intensive medical investigation that revealed nothing, Erasistratus began to look into possible non-medical causes.

A man of the world, he narrowed the possibilities and then, suspecting he was approaching the answer, he requested that the ladies of the court pass the bedside of the prince. As they filed by, the noted physician shrewdly kept his finger on the prince's pulse. As Stratonice passed the bedside the lethargic rhythm leaped to a wild beat, and Erasistratus had the answer.

Seleucus proved to be an understanding father. When the cause of Antiochus' illness was revealed to him, he promptly divorced his young wife and arranged for her immediate marriage to his son. As might be expected, the young man recovered in time for his wedding.

This legend created a new medical classification, a rapid arterial throb called the "lover's pulse."

In his later years, Erasistratus settled on the island of Samos. There, at the age of about 70, he ended his life with poison after developing an incurable ailment. Suicide was a common practice among the aged and infirm of that era. His last words were said to have been: "I die happy in that I have served my country."

After the death of Erasistratus, Alexandrian medicine began to decline. In Ptolemaic Egypt as in the rest of the Western world, superstition, mysticism and magic revived and ended the interlude of critical experiment, adventurous investigation and free thought. Traditionalism and dogma took over once more.

Chapter Eight The Paradox of Galen

Any picture of Galen must be framed in a series of paradoxes.

He was a bridge and a barrier. But for him, the work of the Greek physicians might have been lost. Yet, because of his work, medicine and the investigation of blood came to a virtual standstill for more than a thousand years.

Galen was an original thinker who stifled original thought. He was one of the most thorough experimenters and investigators of his time. His observation that the arteries *did* carry blood was one of the great contributions of the classical era. Yet his purpose was to organize medicine so rigidly that his work would suffice for all time, making further research and experiment unnecessary.

Although Galen lived and died under the Greco-Roman gods, he tended toward a Judaic monotheism. And his medical beliefs so closely fitted the theology of Judaism, Islam and Christianity, that to dispute Galen became a form of heresy.

He disdained the pulse as a measure of emotion yet he used it as a lie detector. When wealthy Romans claimed to be too poor to pay his fees, Galen checked their pulse rates to determine whether they were lying.

Galen flourished in an empire that had replaced Greek individualism and creative imagination with Roman practicality, efficiency and organization. Like other aggressively practical peoples who were to follow, the Romans looked upon intellectualism with distrust, and considered idealism to be decadent if not downright effeminate. They were far more interested in techniques than in theories, in immediate results than in questing research. Roman doctors were fairly effective general practitioners who mixed magic with pragmatism. They had practically no scientific medicine and their knowledge of the blood was very limited.

In such rocky soil, Greek science, medicine and thought could neither root easily nor put out new blossoms. The doctrines and methods introduced by the Greeks were received with suspicion and scorn. This hostility was typified by Cato the Elder, Rome's great cabbage-loving patriot, who believed that Greek medicine was part of a carefully contrived plot to destroy the empire by killing off the Romans. "I forbid you," Cato told his son, "any dealing with Greek doctors."

Despite opposition and hostility, Greek medicine gradually made its way into Rome and, because it was relatively effective, gained some esteem. But it never attained the level it had reached in Alexandria. Shorn of its experimental drive and vitality, it wedded with Roman folk medicine and began to spend itself in a welter of semi-magical doctrines. Here and there a few physicians—such as Celsus—made positive contributions to healing, but the overwhelming atmosphere was one of clashing dogmas and cults.

Claudius Galenus, commonly known as Galen, was born into this Roman world about 131 A.D. His birthplace was Pergamos, a Roman colony in Asia Minor which was celebrated for a medical school, an ancient library and a temple dedicated to Aesculapius.

Galen's father, an engineer named Nicon, was a gentle, cultured man whose life had been made miserable by an emotionally-disturbed wife. His tempestuous home life probably led Nicon to name his son with a form of the Greek word *galenos*, which signifies calm. Galen himself described his mother as ". . . so ill-tempered that she sometimes bit her servant maids."

By all accounts, Galen was a brilliant youth with a quick and eager mind. He received his early education from his father and, by the time he was 15, he was well advanced in the sciences, logic and philosophy. Nicon wanted his son to be a philosopher, but one night, according to legend, Aesculapius appeared before Nicon and pleaded with him to permit his son to become a physician. Dreams were taken very seriously in those days, and Nicon thereupon prevailed upon Galen to focus his attention upon medical and anatomical studies.

Galen attended the medical school in his native Pergamos, studying under teachers who were devoted followers of the Hippocratic cult. Nicon died when Galen was 20; and the young man, with nothing to keep him home, set out on a series of travels to enlarge his knowledge.

First he went to Smyrna where he studied under Pelops, a noted anatomist. Then he traveled to Greece and studied in Corinth. Finally he came to Alexandria, his goal, where the university still stood and where anatomy—Galen's major interest—was still taught.

This was not the Alexandria of the first Ptolemy. Five centuries had passed since Herophilus and Erasistratus. The vigorous research and creativity that had marked that earlier Alexandria had been diminished if not entirely swept away. Dissection of the human body was forbidden. Instead the students at Alexandria tried to unravel the mysteries of the human body from a study of hogs, apes and other animals.

Galen, working on animals, made the understandable assumption that their organs were identical with those of humans. A number of his observations disagreed with those of Herophilus and Erasistratus who had worked on humans, and Galen—whose self-esteem was monumental—assumed that his distinguished predecessors had been abysmally ignorant. It may well have been at Alexandria that Galen set out to obliterate the work of Erasistratus, whom he despised for having contradicted Hippocrates.

When Galen returned to his native Pergamos he was 28 years old and probably one of the best educated physicians of his time. In addition to his great intellectual attainments he unquestionably had another important gift, the ability to ingratiate himself with those who could benefit him or advance his career.

In Pergamos, the Romans had erected an arena where gladiatorial games were held every summer. The official who presided at these games happened to be the high priest of the local temple of Aesculapius. Somehow, Galen so impressed this high priest that he was appointed physician to the gladiators. This position, one of great importance and prestige, gave him an unexpected opportunity to treat shattered limbs and torn bodies.

Galen's record with the gladiators was distinguished, to say the least. During the first summer many were wounded but all of them recovered. This was so unusual that it seemed to verge on the miraculous. One of Galen's innovations at the games was the use of a bandage soaked in wine, foreshadowing the antiseptic dressing of later times.

Galen's term as gladiatorial physician expired in the year 161, and he left for Rome, preceded by a soaring reputation, to set himself up in practice. The capital was then a jumble of mystical healing fads, each supported by a clique pretending to have exclusive philosophical authority. Healing was not even a serious art, let alone a science.

In all this, Galen glowed like a gem of pure reason. A fine physician, he rapidly developed a large practice and a circle of influential friends. His energy was enormous. Single-handed, he set out to reform Roman medicine and put it on what he believed to be a scientific basis.

He might have succeeded had he not been so devout a follower of Hippocrates. Instead of venturing forth in search of new knowledge, he set out to purify the teachings of the Master of Cos, organize them and systematize them into a medical system to endure for the ages. No doctor would ever again have to puzzle over the significance of a particular symptom or wonder which of several possible treatments might be most effective. The Galenic system would take everything into account and provide the correct answer for every situation.

Such an approach, highly organized and authoritarian, neatly fitted Roman philosophy. Even Cato, had he lived, would have understood and appreciated it. But the Roman physicians, whose medical absurdities were thus put under attack, turned against Galen.

Galen ignored the opposition and went about developing his system in a highly scientific way. He performed countless experiments, dissected and lectured in public before growing audiences and wrote a ceaseless stream of medical papers. As his authority and influence grew among the Roman elite, he intensified his attacks on the teachings of Erasistratus and any others whose doctrines conflicted with his interpretation of Hippocrates.

Galen could tolerate no contradiction and he spared no one who disagreed, least of all his contemporaries. According to various historians, he was overbearing, conceited and insufferable with those he considered inferior. As for Roman medical fraternity, he held it in utter contempt. In one of his typically vituperative statements he called them "consummate idiots and poisoners."

Five years after he arrived in Rome, Galen suddenly returned to Pergamos. According to some reports, he fled Rome because of the approach of the great plague that was to bear his name—fearing that his reputation would be damaged by the massive invasion of illness. Another story, apparently supported by Galen himself, suggests that he fled Rome because his irate colleagues were plotting to have him murdered.

In 169 A.D. Emperor Marcus Aurelius summoned Galen to Rome because the great talents of the physician were needed in a military campaign. Galen, reluctant to go marching off with the legions, instead prevailed upon Aurelius to appoint him medical guardian to the heir apparent, Commodus.

This sinecure gave Galen imperial protection from his fellow physicians. And he still had ample time to study, experiment and maintain a private practice. He even instituted what was probably the first mail-order medical business in history. Patients as far away as Spain and Asia wrote, detailing their case histories and symptoms. Galen made his diagnosis and wrote back prescribing the treatment.

During this period of tireless activity Galen completed an estimated 400 works. These constitute the high point in the history of classical medicine. Only about 83 remain although others, attributed to him, do exist and still more have recently been found in Arabic translations. Perhaps, as more of his work is brought to light, Galen's image will take on different contours.

In his exploration of the circulation, Galen made a single great discovery. He found—and emphasized—that the arteries did carry blood. This, he held, was a primary function of the arteries, not merely the result of some accident. Had this observation been added to those of Erasistratus, the complete circulatory system might have been described fourteen centuries sooner.

Apart from this discovery, Galen perpetuated an otherwise strange concept of the blood's circulation. He maintained that after food was digested in the stomach it was brought to the liver where it was converted into blood. But this blood did not circulate. Instead, it ebbed and flowed as needed through the system, carrying portions of the pneuma, or soul, to the various parts of the body.

Galen's beliefs regarding the soul eventually had great religious as well as medical implications. He declared that the soul consisted of three parts. One was the natural spirit, carried in the blood flowing out of the liver, which concerned itself with growth, nutrition and generation. Another was the vital spirit, providing warmth and life to all parts of the body, and carried in the blood that flowed out of the heart. The final portion of the soul was the animal spirit which controlled sensation and movement. This was seated in the brain and was transmitted by the nerves.

The attractions of this particular medico-mystical doctrine of soul were so great in a theological sense, that the total Galenic medical system was ultimately armed with the force of dogma. Consequently, even the absurdities were perpetuated, including the belief that the blood flowed from the right side of the heart directly to the left side by passing through "invisible pores" in the septum, a wall dividing the two ventricles of the heart. This error, accepted as unassailable truth, effectively erased the so-nearly-correct picture of the circulation propounded by Erasistratus.

Galen died in Rome in the year 201, convinced that he had solved all medical problems for all time. He was sure that, with his work to guide them, physicians would no longer have any unanswered questions. "I have continued my practice on until old age," he wrote, "and never as yet have I gone far astray whether in treatment or prognosis as have so many other doctors of great repute. If any one wishes to gain fame. . . . all that he needs is, without more ado, to accept what I have been able to ascertain through zealous research."

For Rome, and for the centuries that followed its collapse, Galenic thought held an almost hypnotic fascination. To the practical Romans it provided a cherished system. To physicians who had to survive in an era of insecurity, it offered a haven of medical certainty.

Galen's assumption that the soul was preeminent and the body only its instrument gave, as we have seen, such firm support to the theology of the Jews, Arabs and Christians that, until the Renaissance, it was considered heretical to question Galen or put his anatomical or medical theories to experimental test.

So, after more than 3,000 years beginning with Athotis and ending with Galen, man found himself knowing less about the river of life than he had probably known at the start.

Chapter Nine

Darkness Descends on the River

In 125 A.D. the Mediterranean world was swept by a pestilence that may have been bubonic plague. Following an invasion of locusts that brought widespread famine, it took over a million lives in North Africa alone. A Roman army sent to defend the city of Utica was completely wiped out.

In the year 164 a new plague—bubonic or typhus—carried by Roman troops, swept across the entire empire. This pestilence, known as the Plague of Galen, ravaged the empire for sixteen years. The next scourge, probably smallpox, struck in 251 and raged for some fifteen years. Then, less than half a century later, another murderous wave of smallpox swept across the Roman world.

Pounded by waves of mounting disaster, the already decaying Roman Empire was placed under a shattering strain. The meagre medical defenses, without the modern weapons of immunology, collapsed. From within the empire was being torn apart by the bankruptcy of a social and economic system based on slavery, by intellectual and moral decadence, and by a series of profitless wars fought more and more by foreign mercenaries.

Tax gatherers put an increasing squeeze upon the poor to pay for the burdens of war. Inflation grew and poverty spread. Roman agriculture, never very highly developed, found itself less and less able to produce food as efficiently as the people whose lands the Romans had conquered.

The political and social systems became paralyzed and government began to lose its centralized control as communications progressively disintegrated. Small communities, forming around the villas of independent landowners, became centers of local production and barter. These were the roots of a feudal society.

Then, from the dark Teutonic forests to the north and the vast Asian grasslands to the east, came the final deluge of disaster. Goths, Vandals, Huns and other so-called barbarians came smashing down in successive massive migrations. They inundated the dying Roman Empire and finally swept it away.

The people of the Mediterranean basin wracked by chaos, impoverished and demoralized by hunger, disease and war, turned in growing numbers to the mystical and messianic cults that flowed out of the Near East. The credulous and the despairing reached desperately for the supernatural salvation that asked only faith, and found an enormous emotional attraction in the new beliefs.

The god, Seraphis, for a while won a large following. The Seraphic worshippers believed that their god raised the dead and was the "saviour and leader of souls" who will save those who followed him and, after death, take them in the "care of his providence." The Seraphic communicants, worshipped not only the aspects of Seraphis, the father, and Horus, the son, but also the mother Isis as she held the infant Horus.

The cult of Aesculapius the Saviour evolved out of the earlier healing cult. In the 4th century it was finally displaced by Christianity. The statues of Aesculapius were removed from their shrines and taken to Christian temples where they were worshipped as images of Christ, the Saviour, who could cure all ills, physical as well as moral, and who offered salvation from the evils, hardships and injustices of the world.

Christianity, at first the faith of the poor and oppressed, steadily spread to other groups. By the early part of the 4th century it had become one of the most potent and well-organized forces in the Mediterranean world, a continent of religious unity in a sea of turmoil.

The Emperor Constantine the Great, who was baptized on his deathbed in 337, saw Christianity's potential unifying power. He officially recognized Christianity in 313 A.D., an act which had a profound effect on human history in virtually all of its aspects including that of scientific investigation. Constantine hoped to preserve the crumbling empire which he was in the process of reorganizing. Where political weapons had proved futile, he was convinced the binding force of the new faith would succeed.

Since differences of theological opinion threatened to blunt the sharp edge of authority desired by Constantine, he convened the council of Nicaea in the year 325. It was the first complete gathering of Christian leaders ever held. The site of the meeting was the town of Nicaea in Asia Minor, just across the Bosphorus from the Byzantine city of Constantinople which was being built to become the new capital of the Roman Empire.

Although he was not yet baptized, Constantine presided over the congress from a golden throne. The Council was stormy and, according to Bishop Eusebius who attended, even violent. At the end, it endorsed the Holy Trinity and the divinity of Christ, and rejected such minority views as Arius's. Later Arius was denounced as a heretic.

Christianity spread rapidly. Zealous missionaries carried it into Armenia, Persia and even such distant places as Germany, Ireland, India and China. And with Christianity came its dogmas. The pagan and other beliefs with which it came into contact had to be overcome, eliminated or absorbed. The earlier classical teachings of the Greeks and Egyptians had already been rejected. Now the teachings of Galen and Aristotle, although they later became dogma themselves, were denounced as pagan.

All forms of scientific investigation, experiment and philosophic questioning were opposed because they cast doubt on the tenets of Christian faith which represented the ultimate truth—beyond reason, knowledge or even the evidence of the senses. "I believe *because* it is absurd!" declared Tertullian, thus dramatizing the conflict between faith and reason.

The medicine of the early Christians, rooted in faith rather than in science, brought to a halt the exploration of the river of life in the West. And the knowledge that had already been won was blotted out by dogma.

Christianity taught that Jesus was the gentle healer of both body and soul. This lifted the odium of sin or uncleanliness that had been frequently associated with sickness. And, since those who suffered were held to be in God's grace, a cure could be had through faith. The Church had decreed that canonical writings bore the stamp of indisputable authority in matters of science as well as faith, and the Epistle of St. James provided a groundwork for the techniques of early Christian medicine:

"Is any sick among you? let him call for the elders of the church; and let them pray over him, anointing him with oil in the name of the Lord:

"And the prayer of faith shall save the sick, and the Lord shall raise him up. . . ." (James 5:14,15)

The medicine of early Christianity grew around these beliefs. There was no need to study the nature of disease, the anatomy of the body or the causes and possible prevention of illness. Disease was cured by the intervention of divine power, through prayer, laying on of hands and anointing with holy oil. Similar practices persist today among Fundamentalist believers in the United States.

Care of the sick was a matter of great religious concern to the Christian. In the climate of war, pestilence and famine that attended and followed the collapse of Rome, the sanctuaries of the religious orders were the only islands of peace where the ill could receive help. Medicine became largely monastic, religious orders were established which took upon themselves the tasks of succoring the sick as an act of piety.

Monastic hospitals and hospices were set up throughout the Christian world. The medicine practiced in them was that propounded by St. James, with magical and mystical elements from the Germanic tribes and the Orient. Disease once more became supernatural in origin. Demons had to be exorcised, and specific saints were invoked as part of the treatment. Saint Job had a special power over leprosy, Saint Lucia over diseases of the eye. The relics of the healing saints—a bone, a fingernail paring or even a shred of clothing—were potent charms against disease. Revelation triumphed over science in the world that had once been enclosed by the Roman eagles. Except in a few outposts of learning, man's thirst for understanding of the worlds around him and within him was quenched with faith.

In such sanctuaries as the monastery founded at Monte Cassino by St. Benedict (on the site of a temple of Apollo which he had ordered pulled down) some of the ancient manuscripts of the pagan scientists were preserved and studied in their Latin translations. This monastery was destroyed in World War II after the Nazis had turned it into a fortress. The monastery near Squillace founded in 538 by the philosopher-physician Cassiodorus also preserved some ancient documents. But even in these citadels, man's mind could only range backward to explore the past. Man's present was not for questioning.

Classical science was demolished with the triumph of orthodoxy. It might have been wiped from the memory of man had it not been for a strange paradox arising out of the very completeness of that victory. Beginning with the unitarian heresy of Arius, the Christian church effectively rooted out dissent. One of these theological heresies was that of Nestorius, Patriarch of Constantinople. He believed that the divine and human natures of Christ were separate; therefore, Mary could not be called "the Mother of God."

Nestorius and his followers, driven into exile, found refuge in the Near East, Persia, Syria, India and even as far away as China. Wherever they took refuge they set up churches and, in 483, they officially split away from the Orthodox church at Constantinople.

In their flight into Asia, the Nestorians carried with them what remained of Greek civilization. They salvaged books of Aristotle,

Hippocrates, Galen and others and translated them into the languages of the lands where they settled.

The Nestorians also set up schools in Syria and Mesopotamia where they taught medicine, philosophy and science from their classical manuscripts. In the middle of the 6th century, a group of Nestorian Christians settled in the Persian city of Jundishapur. The king, appreciative of the knowledge they brought, allowed them to set up a university. Jundishapur, where the works of Galen were taught along with those of Susruta, the great physician of India, soon became a great international medical center.

Thus, as the shadows lengthened over the West, the heritage of Western knowledge was carried to the East and there preserved for the generations to come.

Mohammed and the explosive spread of Islam was a major factor in the strange odyssey of Greek learning. The new faith was simple, direct and personal with a deep brotherly appeal to all men. It taught a strict monotheism and had no church or clergy as such. The mosque served as a place of common prayer and as a court where an *imam*, versed in the Koran, could either preach or expound the law as expressed in the Islamic scripture.

By 632, only five years after the death of Mohammed, Islam had defeated the Persians and was spreading rapidly in all directions. By the 8th century, the Islamic world reached from India and Central Asia across North Africa to Spain. And with Islam, which at this time was a literate religion with each man expected to be able to read and understand the Koran, came a common culture and literary language—Arabic.

The early Muslims were intensely interested in learning, in science and in medicine. Islamic teachings endorsed this interest with religious fervor. "Science lights the path to Paradise. Take ye knowledge even from the lips of an infidel. The ink of the scholar is more holy than the blood of the martyr."

Under Arab rule the University of Jundishapur received government subsidies for the translation of Greek, Judaic, Indian and other available scientific and medical works into the common Arabic tongue. The city of Bagdad, founded in 762, rapidly became a center of learning comparable to Athens. The Calif al-Mamun set up a bureau of translation to translate Aristotle, Ptolemy, Galen and the other Greeks. Astronomy, mathematics and chemistry were protected and subsidized by wealthy merchants and the government. Scientists, doctors and scholars of many nations and religious persuasions were welcomed. Persians, Jews, Greeks, Indians, Egyptians and others came to learn, to teach and to exchange knowledge.

While Europe groped through the Dark Ages, Arab science developed the system of numbers we use today, algebra (al jebr) and the symbol for zero which were derived from Indian mathematics, trigonometry and chemistry.

The great Islamic physicians—Jews and Arabs alike—were gifted and effective healers. But, because religious regulations forbade human dissection, anatomical knowledge and the investigation of the blood came to a standstill.

At least it seems so from the available record. It is possible that advances were made of which we know nothing. Only a small part of Arab medical and scientific work has been translated into Western languages, and this deals mainly with the Greek heritage. A considerable amount of original Arab work and Arab writings derived from the Persians, Indians and others has been largely ignored.

This gap in our knowledge came into focus in 1933 with the translation of a book written in the 13th century by the chief physician of Egypt, Ibn an-Nafis. Ibn took sharp issue with the mistaken opinion of Galen that the blood passed from the right side of the heart directly to the left side through pores in the septum—the wall separating the ventricles.

Instead, this remarkable Arab physician—so little known to the West—correctly traced the flow of the blood from the right side of the heart to the lungs where it was aerated, and thence its return to the left side of the heart. This description of the lesser circulation—probably made from animal studies—predated a similar Western "discovery" by three hundred years and might have been of inestimable service to the later explorers of the circulation had they only known about it.

In the Near East and in Palestine, the Crusades brought clashes of armies and meetings of cultures. In Spain, the Arab world, with its universities and great libraries, touched upon the Christian world. Europeans, steeped in dogmatic medicine and religious mysticism came into close contact with Arab science and medicine and gradually rediscovered a birthright which had been enriched by the many peoples of Islam. So the classical knowledge that had been rooted out and expelled, now began to filter back to Europe after an exile of many centuries. It was carried by pilgrims, soldiers, members of religious orders such as the Hospitalers and by wandering scholars. The darkness that had pressed over Europe began to thin.

Early in the 11th century, a Carthaginian physician named Constantine made a major contribution to the return of classical knowledge to the West. Apparently he was not especially successful as a healer, but as a traveller he achieved great distinction. For thirty-nine years he wandered through the Arab world, studying medicine, reading and collecting books. When he finally returned to his native city he found that he was intensely unpopular. His fellow citizens could neither like nor trust a man who had spent so much time among foreigners, so they decided to kill him. Constantine barely escaped with his life. He stowed away on a ship for Salerno where he found a precarious safety disguised as a beggar.

One day, despite his disguise, he was recognized by a visiting Eastern prince and introduced into the court of Salerno. He was honored as a widely-traveled scholar but court life was not to his taste so he finally retired to the Benedictine monastery at Monte Cassino. There he devoted himself to the translation of the great medical classics from Arabic into Latin.

These works were made available to the medical school at

Salerno which promptly became a center of learning boasting the first medical faculty in the West.

The medical material transmitted through the Arab writings was so superior to the monastic medical doctrines of Europe that it gratified the thirst for fresh knowledge. This is largely why the pupils of Salerno created nothing new —they were sufficiently satisfied to learn and elaborate on the medical wisdom of the ancient Greeks.

Another treasure of Arab writings fell into Christian hands late in the 11th century when the city of Toledo was wrested from Islam by Alfonso VI, King of Castile. This great Moorish city was a center of Mohammedan science and medicine with excellent libraries and a number of scholars who were accomplished linguists. Gerard of Cremona, a remarkable scholar, came to Toledo late in the 12th century, learned Arabic and then made a number of fabulous discoveries in the libraries.

Gerard organized and trained teams of translators from among pupils who flocked around him. Within a few decades, these scholars returned to the West the remaining works of Aristotle and Euclid and many unknown works of Galen and Hippocrates.

Thus, almost a thousand years after the death of Galen, his teachings and those of the earlier Greeks returned to a reawakening Europe. It was an ancient and outdated knowledge, elaborated and refined through centuries of Arabic preservation, but to the Europeans it seemed new, fresh and filled with the tang of intellectual excitement.

From the standpoint of the Church, the teachings of Galen and Aristotle possessed singular merit. Faith and divine revelation no longer sufficed to meet the problems of astronomy, cosmology and biology. Nor could disease be considered a purely religious affair that merely required an act of faith to effect a cure. Faced with a growing dilemma, the Church endorsed the teachings of Aristotle which, by holding that the earth was the center of the universe and that man was the center of life, supported Christian theology. For similar reasons the Church endorsed the medical writings of

Galen who taught the Hippocratic doctrine of the humours and supported the idea that the body was merely the vehicle of the soul.

The teachings of Galen and Aristotle became part of the body of Christian dogma, unquestionable and irrefutable. Western man, long drained of knowledge, regained his thirst. But the well at which he was permitted to drink contained only brackish water. Soon he began to seek a fresher draught.

Part Three THE Rebirth of Thought

Chapter Ten The Past Is Challenged

Darkness enveloped the river of life. Before man could even attempt to breach this darkness two vast realms of knowledge had to be discovered and explored. One realm was the course of the blood—where and how it flowed through the body. The other realm was the substance of the blood and its many purposes.

There were problems all along the way. In order to explore, trace and understand the course of the circulation, a careful development of anatomical studies was needed. These studies in turn would be meaningless without some knowledge of physics, especially of mechanics and hydraulics. Without this, man could not recognize and relate the pumping action of the heart and arteries to the purpose and operation of the circulatory valves.

Nor could man complete his map of the circulation until he

recognized the invisible capillaries. These had already been guessed at by Erasistratus and some of the other early explorers. But guesses, however brilliant, were not enough. The capillaries actually had to be seen, traced, studied, and at least partially understood. Since the capillaries were too small to be seen unaided, all this had to await the invention of the microscope.

But the microscope could hardly be invented without some prior knowledge of the science of optics as well as a technology capable of making and grinding optical glass. Finally, the microscope could not easily be invented and used in a culture which held physical reality to be an illusion and which punished as heresy or diabolism any attempt to study the physical world in other than mystical terms.

The difficulties of investigating the nature and substance of the blood were just as formidable.

To understand the structure and nature of the blood, a high order of chemistry and biochemistry, as well as a science of physiology were required. No less important was the need for scientific instruments. The technologies to produce these did not exist at the beginning of the Renaissance.

There is a fundamental relationship between human progress and the level of man's society at any given moment in history. Great men have made discoveries and evolved theories far in advance of their times. But these, such as the steam engine of Hero of Alexandria or the circulatory theories of Erasistratus, were not and could not be integrated into the mainstream of human advance simply because the culture was not then capable of absorbing them.

Nor can some discoveries be made until the culture has reached a level that makes them feasible and statistically more probable. The microscope is a case in point.

Man and his culture are mirrored in one another. The Renaissance dawned gradually as more and more men, prodded by new and accumulating experience, risked asking questions. It was not a quiet time. For every man willing to challenge the future, many staunchly defended the past, which they saw as their unchanging present. The almost imperceptible process of change in man was reflected by changes in the cultural environment. These developments in turn prodded man with new challenges, and so the process accelerated inexorably, each step gaining nourishment from the step before.

After more than a thousand years of the Christian era the profound influence of the church upon medicine slowly declined. The number of secular physicians increased steadily. Their treatment ranged from unabashed magic to the refined Galenic medicine practiced by skilled Jewish and Arab doctors. Even the monastic healers began to concentrate more on Galen and less on St. James.

Since many of the ailing could not make their way to the hospices established by the religious orders, the priestly physicians left their sanctuaries and began moving out into the world to seek their patients. At last, in growing numbers they established themselves at the courts of kings and princes. Many became more involved in worldly affairs than in the healing of ills or the salvation of souls, and eventually the leaders of the church felt compelled to take decisive action. In the year 1139 the Lateran Council issued an edict which forbade priests and monks to practice medicine. This ban was confirmed by Pope Honorius III who even forbade the members of monastic orders to leave their monasteries. With this, the practice of medicine fell entirely into the hands of the laity.

Although it surrendered the practice of medicine, the church did not give up the teaching of the healing art. For a long while the training of physicians remained largely with the monastic medical schools where only a few of the Galenic texts were available for study. However, the monastic schools soon found themselves competing with a growing number of schools that were free of the immediate authority of the church.

The great school at Salerno which had been so enriched by Constantine of Carthage, was one of the first of these non-clerical teaching centers. This school was supposedly founded in the 9th century when a Greek, a Roman, an Arab and a Jewish physician decided to collaborate on a book of prescriptions and medical treatments. Young men, avid for medical knowledge, gathered around these four physicians and so the Salernan school began.

Before Constantine, Salerno taught virtually nothing beyond the accepted medicine of the Dark Ages. Anatomical studies were ludicrous where they existed at all. Once each year a pig was cut open and his viscera exhibited to the students. When the long exiled classical knowledge was uncovered by Constantine, Salerno entered its most glorious period. True, it taught little that had not been known for centuries to the Arabs and Jews, but to Western students it became a beacon of new knowledge and a model for other medical schools that were arising through Europe.

The year 1240 was a notable one for Salerno and for medicine: Emperor Frederick II, King of Sicily and Jerusalem, decreed a set of rigid standards for the study of medicine, and conferred upon the Salernan school the sole right to license qualified physicians to practice.

Before any man could receive this license he had to fulfill specific minimum requirements. After three years of pre-medical studies, a student had to learn medicine for five years. Following this, for at least one year he had to practice under the supervision of an experienced physician. When this internship was completed, he was granted a license to practice on his own if he then received the approval of the authorities at Salerno. So the first system of organized medical study outside of the church was established. The pattern spread to such great schools as the Universities of Padua and Bologna in Italy, Paris and Montpelier in France and Oxford in England.

Measurable standards of learning had been set. Here and there a few men found these standards a goal to be challenged and exceeded. Still, progress was delayed because of a ridiculous prevailing human attitude. Physicians were still considered men of learning who could only demean themselves by working with their hands. Consequently surgery and the actual work of dissection that was necessary to the study of anatomy was left to lesser men who required no great study.

As it happened, the practice of surgery became largely a sideline of the barbering profession. This was absurd. Before a man was deemed competent to treat an attack of indigestion he needed nine years of schooling and a license. But an amputation or the cutting open of a body, since it was a form of manual labor, was left to an unschooled barber-surgeon.

The curious evolution of barber into surgeon is directly related to the blood. Ecclesiastic law required that every monk undergo regular bloodletting, probably in the belief that it helped ease the pressure of worldly temptations. Since the barbers came regularly to the monks for tonsure, the barbers—adept in the use of cutting instruments—performed the bleeding as well. By the end of the 11th century barbers were widely accepted as surgeons. In addition to bloodletting, they performed operations and even pulled teeth. Some of these barber-surgeons became highly skilled in their professions and, like Ambroise Paré, achieved great renown.

The attitude toward manual work naturally affected the study of anatomy. The anatomy taught at the burgeoning schools was an improvement over no anatomical studies at all, but only barely. Human dissection was rare where it was permitted at all. And, whether a human or animal cadaver was to be dissected, the professor hired a barber or some other person to do the task. As the corpse was cut open, the teacher would stand aside and read aloud from Galen's work what Galen had decreed would be seen. No attempt was made to allow the students to examine the cadavers for themselves.

The majority of teachers in the years just preceding the Renaissance seemed to consider their task as twofold—imparting the wisdom of the ancients and, at the same time, defending it against any attempts to question or improve upon it.

The nature of the universities themselves, of course, had an important effect upon learning. There were three types of schools.

State universities, such as the one founded at Naples by Frederick II and those in Spain founded by Alfonso VIII, were supported by the rulers and had to comply with government regulations. Other universities such as those at Paris and Oxford, were directly under the rule of the church authorities. The most unusual schools were those supported by their communities. Bologna, Padua and other Italian centers had such universities. They were remarkable for their independence and democratic organization, and they made the greatest initial contribution to man's search for knowledge and understanding. At Bologna the rector of the university was elected by the student body.

Despite this freedom, the church did not by any means abdicate its supervision of education. All universities in Christendom, regardless of how they were organized or who directed them, were under the ultimate power of the Pope and his representatives. They had the right to make all final decisions.

The early schools were unusual in many respects. They did not have elaborate facilities. Any available meeting place for students, taverns and the like, was often the classroom or lecture hall. Occasionally, lectures on anatomy were delivered in brothels.

The path of knowledge was far from smooth. Dogma remained strong and, while a certain latitude of thought was permitted, the punishment for excessive intellectual independence could be terrible. This was grimly demonstrated in the case of an unusually brave and gifted man known as Pietro d'Abano.

Born in 1250, Pietro took his surname from the place of his birth, a spa near Padua noted for its sulphur baths. At the University of Padua, where he studied medicine and philosophy, he proved himself a remarkable Greek scholar.

It was Greek that led d'Abano to greatness and destruction. While he was studying medicine, it occurred to him that the medical classics being used as texts must have lost some accuracy in their translations from the original Greek into Arabic and thence into Latin. A number of the Greek manuscripts were still available, especially in the universities of the Arab world, so d'Abano made up his mind to track down the originals and make his own translations directly from Greek into Latin.

He made extensive translations of various classics, particularly the works of Galen. As was bound to happen to a man of d'Abano's intellectual breadth, this exposure to differing viewpoints led him to weigh truth against truth.

At the University of Paris, where he became a noted instructor, d'Abano used his special gifts and the knowledge he had garnered to write a number of books on medicine, astronomy and other sciences. In his classes, as was expected of him, he taught the wisdom of the ancients. But he differed and disputed with the ancients whenever he thought them wrong. He even went so far as to question some of the teachings of Aristotle.

An outspoken group of students gathered about him, attracted by the vigorous wine of dissent. Before long he became a central figure in the movement against intellectual rigidity. The dread accusation of heresy was not long in coming.

Monastic investigators of the inquisitorial Dominican order pored over his work with exquisite care. They declared fifty-five passages contrary to the Christian dogma, and d'Abano was thereupon denounced to the Holy Inquisition. Among the charges leveled against him were that "He practiced sorcery and necromancy; he did not believe in miracles; he was lukewarm in religious matters."

D'Abano's sorcery and necromancy consisted of scientific experiments and anatomical investigations. Fortunately, he was able to defend himself successfully against the charges and won his release.

He returned to Padua, as a leader of the university faculty. There, despite his experience with the Inquisition, he questioned the medical validity of miraculous cures and courageously continued his investigations into the physical nature of disease. He was again denounced for heresy. D'Abano was seriously ill while his trial was being prepared and he died before it actually began. But the Inquisition was not to be put off. The trial was held over d'Abano's corpse, which was found guilty of heresy and condemned to be burned at the stake. The sentence was carried out with all the ritual required by the solemn occasion.

The manner of Pietro d'Abano's death and immolation was in keeping with the uncertainty of the times. Just as the Roman Empire had collapsed under the accumulated erosion of social and economic decay, external assaults and a deluge of disasters; the medieval world was succumbing to inner and outer attrition. In the 14th century, great plagues again swept across the face of Europe, pitting it with death and desolation. One of these, the massive wave of bubonic plague known as the Black Death, wiped out between a quarter and a half of the total population. The feudal economy began to break down, hunger spread and, out of these and other hardships, there arose a series of peasant wars in which the serfs tried to win freedom and the right to dispose of their own crops.

As the serfs of Central Europe rebelled against the authority of the feudal lord, the barons, princes and kings attempted to break the temporal authority of the Church. Out of these rebellions, which struck against the established symbols of right and power, finally came the Renaissance and Reformation.

Fear of authority began to waver and weaken. It became reasonable and even fashionable—although still perilous—to question dogma. There was a flood of new ideas, a release of long-pent creative energy in literature, the arts and in science.

The Chinese technique of paper making had spread into Europe and, by the 15th century, paper had become cheap enough to make the production of books on a fairly large scale economically practical. With paper, printing developed as part of a logical unfolding of synergistic progress. The spread of knowledge became easier, broader and more rapid.

In this blossoming atmosphere the once-retarded study of anatomy went beyond merely medical needs. Human beauty, the beauty of face, form, mood and movement became a matter of almost mystical importance. Impelled to seek out and express this beauty, more and more people were attracted to the arts, including many of great talent and some of genius. But how could human beauty be interpreted without first studying the human body? Thus the study of anatomy became as important to the artist as it was to the physician. No one who had not studied the human body could be considered an artist.

So the way was prepared for the complex genius of Leonardo da Vinci. Leonardo, who was born in 1452, recognized no boundaries for his thrusting intellect. Considering the man and the times, it was almost inevitable that Leonardo would, in addition to everything else, become one of the prime forces in the renaissance of anatomy and thus one of the important explorers of the river of life. Leonardo possessed the ability to work painstakingly and tirelessly that is one of the characteristics of genius.

According to the Cardinal of Aragon, Leonardo performed at least thirty dissections on the cadavers of males and females of varying ages, making a minute study of their anatomy as well as the sex-related and age-related differences. Ten dissections were performed solely so that he could study the blood vessels. By the time he was through, Leonardo hoped to complete a vast work that would encompass the anatomy of men and women from the fetal stage to old age. On the other hand he paid absolutely no attention to the classical authorities. He ignored Galen, not because he disliked or disputed him especially, but because he insisted on learning for himself.

The most enduring part of Leonardo's anatomical work are the drawings he made of his observations. These have never been matched for artistic perfection and accuracy. But Leonardo was more than a superb artist and anatomist. His enduring greatness lies in the magnificent sweep of his genius. As he studied the human body, he developed techniques that enriched the science of anatomy. As he studied the heart and blood vessels, his understanding of hydraulics and mechanics enabled him to recognize the functions of the valves and helped brush away many of the prevailing absurdities regarding the circulation.

Leonardo's work stands as a monument to the probing force within man that, on occasion, bursts forth like a newborn sun. His anatomical studies were the first ever done in the West that were completely free from dogma and tradition. They were scientific in the finest sense, an utterly objective study of the human body. Unfortunately, like so many other precious human endeavors, it passed into a semi-obscurity from which it was not rescued for several centuries.

In the north of Europe a more austere rebellion, the Protestant Reformation, broke out. The Reformation produced a number of great medical figures, among them the Swiss known as Paracelsus, a strange and unusual man as well as a great physician.

Paracelsus taught at the University of Basel. Instead of defending Galen as was expected of teachers, he assailed him and shook the very foundations of medicine. Outspoken to the point of recklessness, impatient with what he considered error and stupidity, he personified the spirit of revolt.

Paracelsus' real name was Philip Aureolus Theophrastus Bombastus von Hohenheim, and there was certainly bombast in the dramatic way he expressed his humanistic approach to healing. Claiming that medicine killed as often as it cured because physicians clung too closely to the teachings of Hippocrates and Galen, he reputedly piled the works of Galen on the floor of his lecture hall and set them on fire. As amazed students looked on, he told them to forget the dogma of the ancients and go out to learn for themselves. Medicine, he said, could be freed of its worst errors "Not by following that which those of old taught, but by our own observation of nature, confirmed by extensive practice and long experience."

The faculty at Basel, the practicing physicians and authorities generally were horrified and enraged. Paracelsus soon became the target of a mounting wave of accusations, including a whispering campaign declaring him to be a dangerous heretic who deserved to be burned at the stake. In 1528 the stubborn Paracelsus finally realized that even his supporters were afraid to speak to him, so he secretly fled the city of Basel and took refuge in Alsace.

Fear followed him. No longer permitted to teach, he began to write. But as he wandered through Germany, he could not even find a printer who would dare to print his books.

It was not until he died in 1541, at the age of 48, that his supporters found the courage to proclaim themselves openly. Overnight Paracelsus was declared a great reformer in medicine just as Luther was held to be a great reformer in religion. Printers and universities that had previously spurned his work all at once became anxious to bring his writings to the world. Death had washed Paracelsus clean of the danger he carried and made him acceptable to his contemporaries.

So Europe entered its period of rebirth.

Chapter Eleven

The Inquisitive and the Inquisitors

Leonardo da Vinci ignored Galen, and Paracelsus burned his books, but it remained for a physician who was actually devoted to the Greco-Roman master to wrap a shroud around the Galenic anatomy.

This brilliant young man was born in Brussels on the last day of 1514. He became known to the world as Andreas Vesalius—his name being a Latinized version of Wesel, the German town where his family had lived.

With a pharmacist as a father, Andreas became intensely interested in medicine and anatomy. In his boyhood he gathered mice, rats, frogs and birds, dissected them and made careful note of their characteristics. His formal studies began at seventeen and, when he was nineteen, he went to the University of Paris. There he studied anatomy under Jacques Dubois, a noted physician and teacher who was, typically, a devout follower of Galen.

Human dissection was rare at the time, and most of the studies were made on dogs and other animals. Conforming to the mores of the era, Dubois would not think of doing the dissections himself. Such menial labor was far beneath the dignity of a respected physician. So a barber, armed with a razor, dissected while Dubois read to the class the Galenic text concerning the particular part of the body being exposed.

No effort was made to observe the organs and tissues to see whether or not they conformed to the Galenic description. Such irreverence was discouraged because it tended to cast doubt upon all authority. When Dubois came to a portion of the master's text that seemed difficult or obscure he simply skipped over it. In this way the science of anatomy was taught at the University of Paris in the year 1532.

Vesalius was an eager student. On a few occasions when a human corpse was available for dissection, he applied for and received permission to replace the barber. The possibility of saving the fee ordinarily paid to the barber was no doubt an important consideration in Vesalius's favor. So the young Vesalius probed the human body, paying careful attention to everything he saw, while Dubois standing away from the cadaver, read from Galen and pointed out the organs with his cane.

Vesalius could not help but notice certain discrepancies. He could see, for instance, that the lower jaw consisted of only one section. Yet he could hear his professor reading from Galen's text that the lower jaw of the human was constructed of two parts. The young student, evidently wise in the ways of the world, asked no embarrassing questions. Consequently he graduated with honors, having achieved a brilliant record both for scholarship and, more privately, for keeping his doubts to himself.

When Vesalius came to the University of Padua in 1537, it had already acquired the glittering reputation that was attracting students from all over Europe. But Vesalius did not come as a student. Only about twenty-three at the time, he was appointed Professor of Surgery and Anatomy, in recognition of his superior attainments.

Regardless of how he felt personally, Vesalius appeared to be a devotee of Galen. Yet he could not forget the obvious discrepancies he had seen during his dissections. So, taking advantage of the new opportunities for research offered at Padua, he began a careful investigation. Checking the various anatomical writings of Galen against his own meticulous observations of human anatomy he found that Galen's work was filled with errors.

What had been considered a correct picture of human anatomy

for 1,300 years, what had been accepted as dogma by the Church, and what had been taught at Padua for over 300 years, Vesalius found was false. Galenic anatomy was fine for swine, apes or goats but not for humans. Realizing that there had to be a new beginning in the study of anatomy, he set out to do the job himself, making sure that this time human rather than animal cadavers would be used. The undertaking required great courage—physical as well as moral. It was extremely audacious for a man still in his twenties to set out to correct errors that, after more than a thousand years, stood as indisputable truth.

Vesalius began from the beginning, as though Galenic anatomy had never existed. He dissected, experimented, observed and described what he saw with great care and elaborate detail. He did not attack Galen. He merely set out to build a science of human anatomy based on human observations.

The anatomical drawings accompanying Vesalius' work were done by a fellow German named Johann Stephan von Kalkar. It is possible that von Kalkar's drawings were influenced to a certain extent by da Vinci's prior work. But the anatomical studies made by Vesalius himself—although the anatomist probably knew of da Vinci's accomplishment—were unquestionably independent.

An incredible amount of physical labor was involved. Vesalius also needed a constant supply of cadavers for his dissections. Obtaining them was no easy task. He bribed the attendants at charnel houses, bought the corpses of executed criminals and, according to some tales, even resorted to grave robbing.

The colossal task was finished in 1542. Vesalius was still only 27 years old. The following year the results were published in a book entitled *De Humani Corporis Fabrica*. By one of those unique coincidences, just as the anatomy of Galen was demolished, the universe of Aristotle was shaken. A Polish astronomer named Nikolaus Koppernigk, known by the Latinized name of Copernicus, showed that the earth, instead of being the center of the universe, actually revolved around the sun with her sister planets.

So, the two pagan teachings that had become Christian dogma

at about the same time fell the same time—although it was many years before they were finally laid to rest.

The epochal work of Vesalius, in 663 folio pages and more than 300 woodcuts, presented the first complete scientific text on human anatomy in history. In it Vesalius created the anatomical methods that are still in use today. There are some errors in the work, due largely to the fact that Vesalius did not have necessary scientific instruments. But the errors are insignificant compared to the accuracy of the bulk of this work which opened the door to the modern exploration of the circulation.

Now for the first time man had at his command a science and the beginning of a technology that made possible a careful study of the pathways of the blood. Vesalius described the anatomy of the human heart and the course of the veins. He also stated very clearly that he did not see any pores in the septum, the membrane separating the two ventricles of the heart. The Galenic dictum that blood passed from the right to the left side of the heart through invisible pores in the septum had been one of the misconceptions blocking man's understanding of the circulation. Although Vesalius was careful never to make any flat statement declaring Galen to be wrong, he let his observations speak for themselves.

"I do not see," he said, "how even the smallest amount of blood could pass from the right ventricle to the left through the septum."

The publication of Vesalius' work loosed a tempest. The idea that a youngster of twenty-eight, bright though he might be, dared attack the venerable authorities of the past was intolerable. Furthermore, this upstart could demonstrate that his anatomic concepts were correct and anyone repeating the experiments could confirm them for himself. This was a bitter brew for the doctors, teachers and authorities committed to Galen. So they denied that any of Vesalius' statements could possibly be true. Even Jacques Dubois, who had taught Vesalius at Paris and had permitted him to perform his first human dissection, bitterly assailed his former pupil.

Vesalius had raised a storm he had not at all anticipated. Instead of winning acclaim for his precious addition to man's knowledge, he found himself ringed by enemies. Three years after his work appeared, the atmosphere in Padua was so hostile that he left for Spain where he became physician to the royal family. He remained at the Spanish court until 1563 when, still plagued by troubles, accusations and hostility, he left on a pilgrimage to the Holy Land.

Some accounts claim he fled Spain because he performed a dissection upon a living woman. According to this tale, he was working on what he believed to be a cadaver when, as he made an abdominal incision, the "corpse" sat up with a shriek. This was typical of many slanders spread about Vesalius. Curiously, it was very like the calumnies that earlier opponents of dissection had spread about Herophilus and Erasistratus.

In addition to all this, charges of heresy were leveled at Vesalius from many directions. The indications are that his pilgrimage to the Holy Land was for expiation and to avoid an open accusation of heresy. He visited Jerusalem, Mount Sinai and other holy places and then, hopefully shriven, began a return which was abruptly cut off.

A violent storm wrecked Vesalius's ship, casting him upon the Ionian island of Zante. There, wracked by disease and privation, the father of modern anatomy perished.

The death of Vesalius was tragic and unfortunate, but at least accidental. Miguel Servetus, a younger contemporary of Vesalius suffered a much worse fate.

Servetus, born in Villanueva in 1509, was more outspoken and less prudent than Vesalius. A proud, stubborn and strong-minded Spaniard, he actually studied for the priesthood but turned to medicine because it permitted him more freedom to probe and question the existing dogmas.

The fact that Servetus was a theologian as well as a physician contributed largely to the tragedy of his death. He undertook medical studies at Lyons in France then went to Paris where he

1. Hippocrates

2. Galen (130-200 A.D.)

3. Paracelsus (Philippus Aureolus Theophrastus Bombastus von Hohenheim, 1493-1541)

4. Michael Servetus (1511-1553)

5. A doctor bleeding a patient (from the Luttrell Psalter)

6. Henry VIII granting a charter to the Barber-surgeons (by Holbein)

7. Blood-letting, 1513

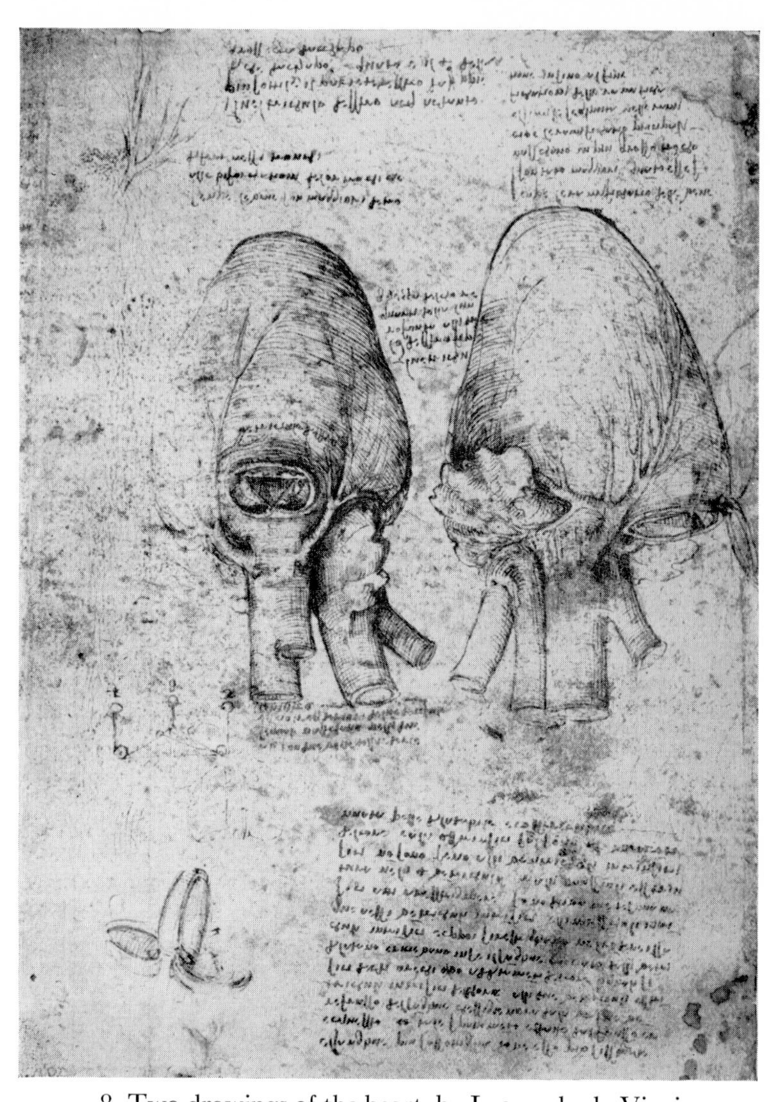

8. Two drawings of the heart, by Leonardo da Vinci

9. Andreas Vesalius (1514-1564)

10. Andrea Cesalpino (1518-1603)

11. Paolo Sarpi (1552-1623)

12. Marcello Malpighi (1628-1694)

13. William Harvey (1578-1657)

14. Harvey demonstrating the circulation of the blood to Charles I

15. Barber-surgeon operating in his office. The stuffed animal—usually an alligator—suspended from the ceiling was intended to keep evil spirits away

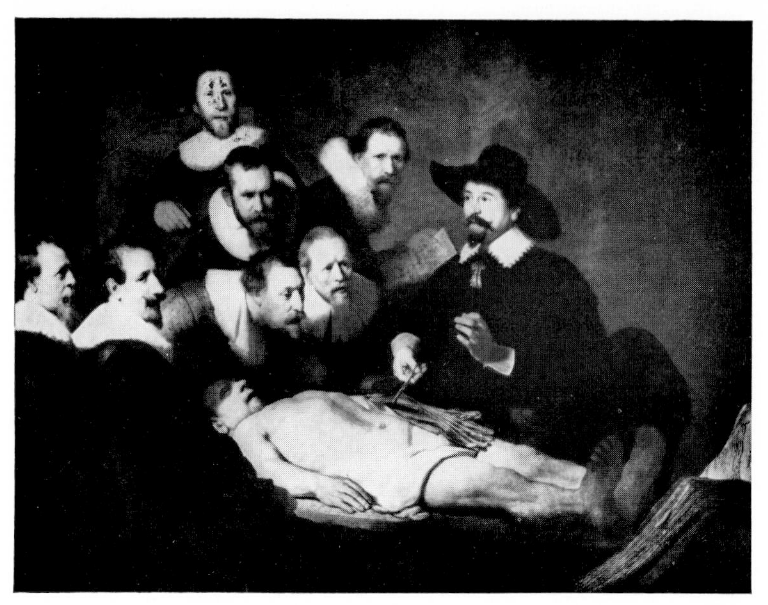

16. "The Anatomy Lesson," by Rembrandt

17. Early blood transfusion—a 17th-century woodcut showing the transfusion of blood from an animal to a man.

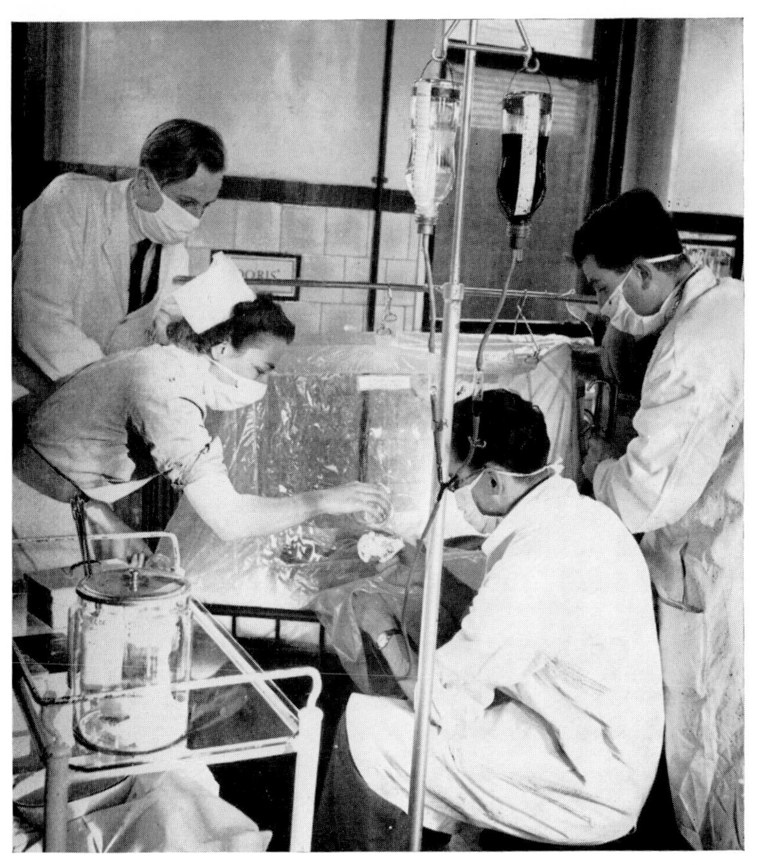

18. A modern blood transfusion—to a baby in an oxygen-tent.

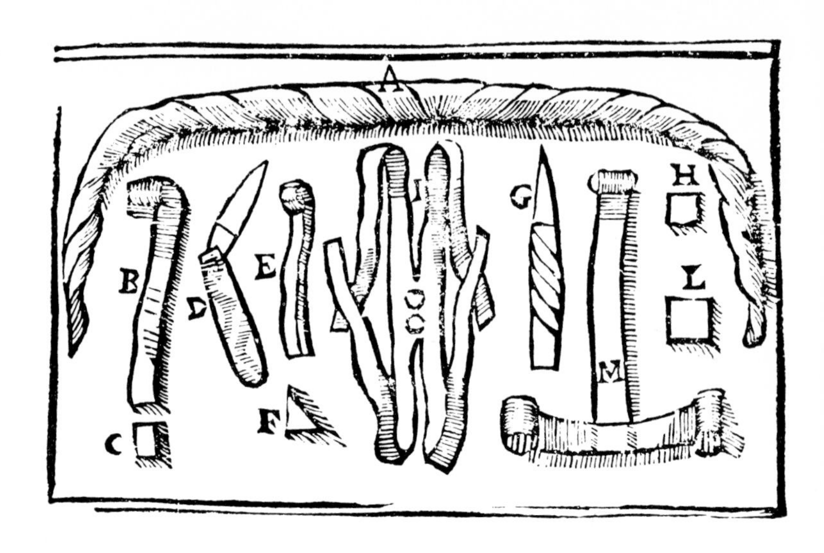

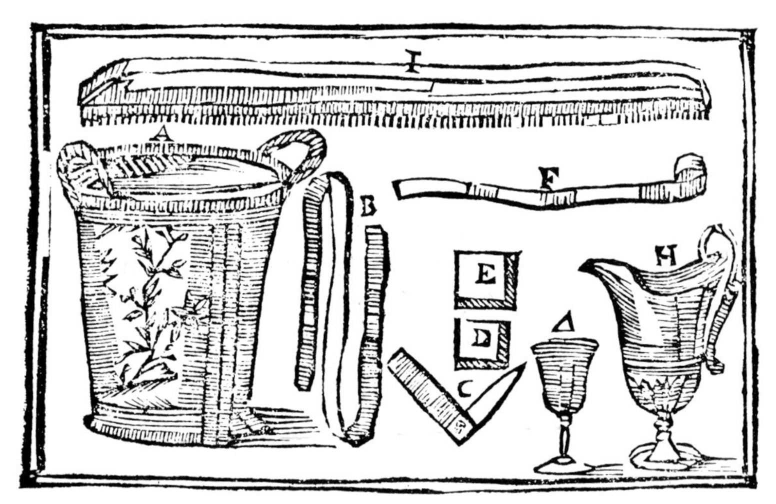

19, 20. 18th-century instruments used for performing a bleed on the head and the foot

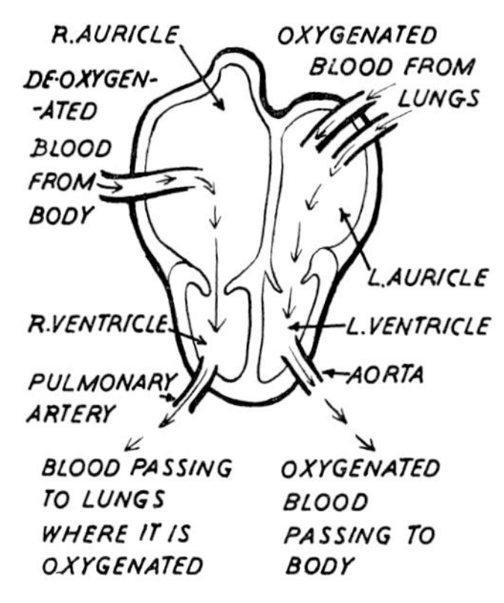

21. Diagrammatic cross-section of the heart.

22. Diagrammatic lay-out of an operating theatre during a heart operation

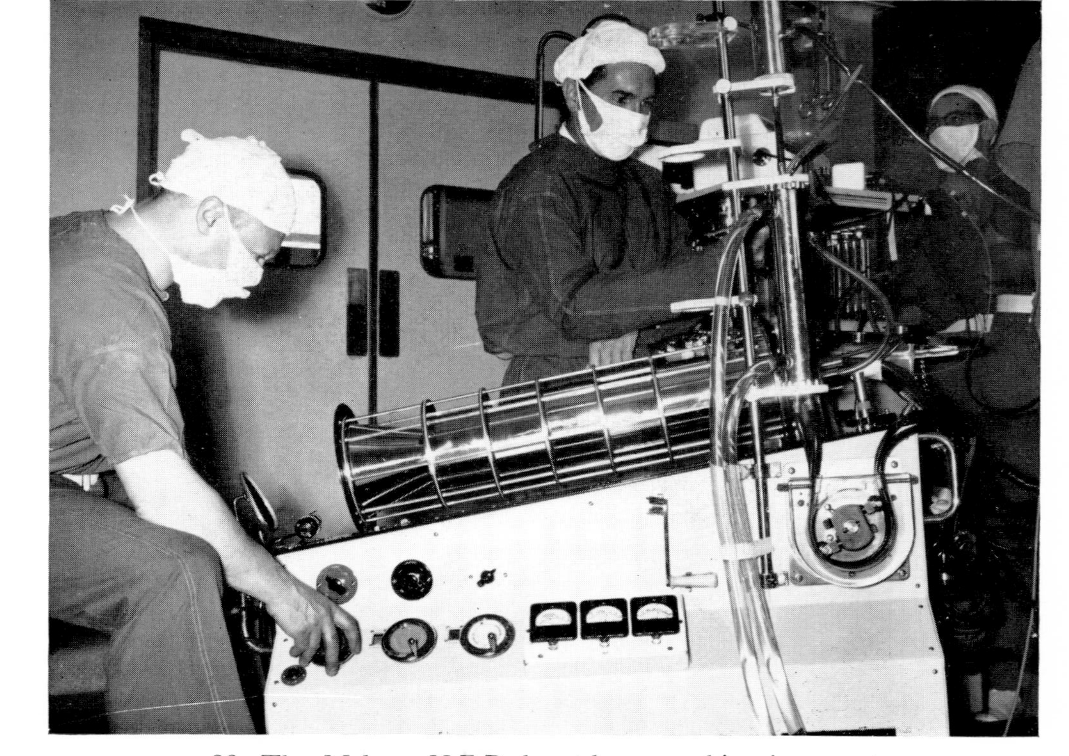

23. The Melrose N.E.P. heart-lung machine in use at Hammersmith Hospital

studied anatomy under the same Dubois who had taught Vesalius. By another wry coincidence, Servetus also succeeded Vesalius in performing the actual dissections while Dubois pointed with his cane as he read from Galen.

Following his graduation, Servetus set up medical practice in France, meanwhile continuing his anatomical studies and his theological inquiries. The result of these labors was a book entitled *Christianismi Restituto*, published in 1546, in which, among other things, he swept away the Galenic doctrine that the blood passed through pores in the septum.

Where Vesalius had simply stated that he found no pores and therefore could not see how the blood might move through the septum, Servetus *showed* that this movement did *not* take place. Furthermore, he outlined what actually happened. His correct hypothesis of the pulmonary circulation was similar to the earlier theories proposed by Erasistratus of Alexandria and by the Arab Ibn an-Nafis.

First of all, Servetus showed that a greater volume of blood entered the lungs through the pulmonary arteries than was actually necessary to nourish the lungs. This led him to a brilliant deduction: The purpose of this apparently excessive flow was to bring the blood to the lungs where it could be aerated. Then the aerated blood returned via the pulmonary veins to the heart from which it was sent out into the body.

"The communication between the right and left ventricle," he wrote, "does not as is generally believed take place through the mid-wall of the heart, but in a wonderful way the subtle blood is conducted through a long passage from the right ventricle to the lungs, where it is rendered light, becomes bright red in color and passes from the vein-like artery(*arteria venosa*) into the artery-like vein (*vena arteriosa*), whence it is finally carried by the diastole (dilation of the heart muscle) into the left ventricle."

Servetus did not do things in half measures. The same book that attacked the medical dogmas of Galen also contained a number of theological opinions that differed from the prevailing orthodoxies.

Among other things, Servetus expressed certain unitarian views which were deemed an heretical attack upon the dogma of the Trinity.

The book caused so great an outcry when it was finally published in Paris that Servetus had to flee for his life. Heading for what he believed might be sanctuary in Italy, he made the mistake of entering the Swiss city of Geneva, a stronghold of the Protestant leader John Calvin.

Calvin, who was seeking to reform Christianity by returning it to an earlier austerity, matched the Inquisition in his dedicated defense of what he believed to be the only truths. So the unfortunate Servetus was seized as he entered the Calvinist citadel, accused of heresy and brought to trial.

The outcome was never in doubt as the trial moved to its inexorable conclusion.

"We condemn thee, Michael Servetus, to be bound and to be led to the place of Shampell, there to be fastened to a stake and burned alive, together with thy heretical book, as well written by hand as printed, even until they be reduced to ashes. And thus wilt thou finish thy days to furnish an example to others who might wish to commit the like."

The sentence was carried out in Geneva on October 27, 1553. Servetus and all but three copies of his book went up in flames.

The effect of Servetus's work is difficult to measure since most of his books were so quickly destroyed. There is no question, however, that a number of his contemporaries and successors knew of his work, discussed it, weighed it and, where they were courageous enough, used it to guide their own advances.

Man and his times were prodding each other forward despite the resistance of the undead past. Each new phase of man's life added to the total effect. A more efficient development of commerce stimulated the science of astronomy. More shipping created a need for better navigation. Better navigation demanded astronomy.

A similar pattern was followed in virtually all areas of human enterprise. In the Netherlands, growing prosperity permitted more people to afford eyeglasses. The boom in the spectacles industry soon made possible the almost inevitable accident that led to the telescope. One story relates that the telescope was discovered when a child in the shop of a spectacles-maker named Lippershey accidentally looked through one lens at another and noticed that this made distant objects seem closer.

The telescope helped prove that the Earth was a minor planet in a solar system revolving around a minor sun. But Galileo Galilei had to recant his findings under the threat of death. A lone old man of sixty-nine, he kneeled before ten cardinals in their ceremonial robes of red, and announced that the evidence of his telescope and his intellect had been false.

The Aristotelian dogma was thus briefly buttressed. But where Galileo recanted, Giordano Bruno facing the Roman Inquisition for a similar heresy, stubbornly insisted that his thoughts were free and that he had the right to draw his own conclusions from the facts available to him. Bruno was reduced to ashes as the 16th century drew to a close.

Part Four THE River Is Mapped

Chapter Twelve The Italians Plot the Course

The 16th century did not accept the idea that the blood circulated at all.

More than four thousand years earlier the legendary Chinese Emperor Hwang-ti had written: "The blood current flows continuously in a circle and never stops. . . ." But this concept of the circulation had withered for lack of comprehension as well as the means of proof. Consequently, it was generally believed that the blood moved through the vessels in a sort of tidal ebb and flow that depended upon the state and needs of the body.

The idea of the lesser, or pulmonary, circulation for which, among other things, Servetus had gone to the stake, began gaining credence in the 16th century. Furthermore, it could be demonstrated. As this concept took hold it provoked new thoughts and questions, so helping to lay the groundwork for the mapping of the total circulation.

Man's achievements are seldom accidental. They are the culminations of many chains of interwoven events—just as a flower bursting suddenly into bloom culminates from seed, soil, climate, root, leaf, bud and countless other sources. And, just as each flower contributes to the next seeding, so does each advance contribute to man's next achievement.

Many factors interacted to create both the intellectual atmosphere and the practical conditions within which the full discovery of the circulation could finally be achieved. Some of these in the Europe of the 16th century were: the gradual freeing of medicine from clerical influence, the steady erosion of the Galenic and Aristotelian dogmas; the resurgence in the study of anatomy; and, finally, the simultaneous advances in science, technology, social and economic organization and in other areas of life and learning.

As though to prove that man's accumulated knowledge and experience had reached a level that made the discovery of the lesser circulation almost inevitable, Servetus' work was duplicated independently by Realdo Colombo.

Colombo, who was born in Cremona in 1510, took over the chair of anatomy at Padua after Vesalius was forced to leave. Shortly thereafter he published his book, *De Re Anatomica.* In this work he attacked the Galenic view of the blood flow in the heart as "absolutely false" and accurately described the lesser circulation. He also made a number of important original observations.

Colombo's scientific work was unquestionably valuable, but its background was tinged with the bitterness of apparent duplicity and betrayal. All men react to pressures, but the reactions differ as the men differ. Even under the strongest pressures some men will retain their humanity while others will sacrifice it, more or less regretfully, to the demands of survival, advancement or whatever prize is at stake.

When Vesalius corrected the Galenic errors, his colleagues at Padua fiercely attacked him. One of the most outspoken of these critics was Colombo himself. Then, as soon as he filled the professorship that Vesalius had been forced to vacate, Colombo reversed himself. He attacked Galen even more directly and pointedly than had Vesalius.

Some historians believe that Colombo had written his book a number of years before but waited for an opportune moment to have it published. In any case, whatever Colombo's timing and his motivations, it is generally agreed that his conclusions were arrived at independently of Servetus's, whose works he had apparently not read.

Describing the lesser circulation, Colombo wrote that "the blood flows through the *vena arteriosa* to the lungs and there it is attenuated; then, mixed with air, it goes through the *arteria venosa* to the left heart, just as everyone may observe, but which no one has observed to this day and no one has stated in his writings."

Had Colombo stopped at this point his contribution to the mapping of the river of life would have been noteworthy if not original. But he went much further. Carefully observing the four great blood vessels of the heart, he noted that two of them were so constructed that they brought blood to the heart while the other two were constructed to carry blood away from the heart. Relating the movement of the blood to the heartbeat, he found that the blood was brought into the heart during diastole—the part of the beat in which the heart dilates, and was pumped out of the heart during systole, the part of the beat in which the heart contracts.

Colombo then showed that the valves in the heart worked to keep the blood flowing in a single direction. When the valves opened, the blood could enter. Then the valves closed "so that the blood cannot flow out in the same way."

Close study of Colombo's work indicates that he deserves more credit than history has given him. In addition to describing the lesser circulation, he must have visualized to a large extent the greater circulation through the body. Yet there were some notable errors of the past that he handed on. One of these was the belief that the veins carried the blood to the body. Another was the idea that the blood was formed in the liver.

The knowledge and understanding of the circulatory valves were clearly a key to the understanding of the circulation itself. Since the valves in the heart and vessels permitted the blood to flow only in a single direction, obviously any ebb and flow through these vessels was impossible. Yet, even though Colombo and others before him had some knowledge of the valves, the obvious somehow eluded them—either because the preconceptions of the time blunted their vision or for some other, more obscure, reasons.

The blood and its possible pathways were increasingly fascinating to physicians and anatomists. Consequently there was overlapping work on similar projects. This situation produced strange forms of cooperation as well as some intense competition, jealousy and even enmity. In at least one case, the result was an intellectual tragedy.

The main figure in this unfortunate affair was Giovanni Battista Canano of Ferrara, a sensitive, shy and withdrawn anatomist of great intellectual gifts. He was the first to describe the valves that functioned in the veins and he was preparing a comprehensive study of anatomy which would have been of incalculable worth had it been completed. This much was apparent from a preliminary section of the work which he had already published when Vesalius's book appeared.

Canano, stunned by the unexpected publication of an anatomical work of such magnitude, was convinced that his own efforts would appear insignificant beside it. Discouraged, depressed and with a profound sense of defeat he not only stopped work on his project but even withdrew from circulation the portion he had completed and published.

What made this a scientific loss of the first order was the fact that Canano's acute observation of the nature of the valves in the veins was not matched by any of his contemporaries. This acuteness, combined with his ability to make bold interpretations, might well have led to an earlier discovery of the circulation. Instead,

Canano passed his information regarding the valves to Vesalius in the expectation that the Paduan professor could achieve much more. But Vesalius, who admitted receiving the data, did nothing about it and so a very precious gift of knowledge was wasted.

His explorations brought to an abrupt close, Canano died in 1577 with his great discovery ignored and virtually forgotten.

What Canano had seen and told Vesalius was that the valves of the veins were so constructed that the blood could not possibly flow into the veins from the heart but only to the heart from the veins. With this information, it should have been obvious that the arteries, not the veins, carried the blood out from the heart to the body and that the veins could only serve to return the blood to the heart.

By the latter half of the 16th century, study of the circulatory valves attracted the concentrated interest of Italy's great anatomists. First they asked the general questions: What were the valves? How did they function? What was their effect? Then, as these questions were answered and the information accumulated, they asked more probing and specific questions.

The anatomist Carlo Ruini, a noted veterinarian of Bologna, devoted himself to the study of horses and wrote a book in which he described the action of the valves within the heart as well as the manner in which the left side of the heart pumped the blood into the system. In Venice, the almost legendary Friar Paolo Sarpi studied the valves of the veins and passed his findings along to his friend Fabrizio d'Aquapendente, professor of anatomy at Padua and the teacher, mentor and sponsor of William Harvey.

The great Fabrizio received his name from the place of his birth, the tiny Tuscan village of Aquapendente where he was born in 1533. He was such a brilliant teacher that students from all parts of Europe were drawn to Padua. Fabrizio was also a renowned surgeon. He made a fortune from his practice, and he used some of it to build an anatomical theatre at Padua, the only Renaissance building of its kind that still is entirely preserved.

Under Fabrizio's guidance the modern science of physiology

received a new and urgent stimulus. Anatomy, of course, deals with the structure of the body and its organs. Physiology takes this a step further by examining the functions of the various body structures and organs. Where anatomy would determine the nature of the heart and its construction, physiology would investigate the purpose of the heart, what it does and how it does it.

Fabrizio achieved great stature both as an anatomist and a physiologist, but he is probably best remembered as the teacher of Harvey and as the anatomist who gave the first public demonstration of the valves of the veins. He described these to his students in the following words: "Little doors of the veins is the name I give to certain very thin little membranes occurring on the inside of the veins. . . . They have their mouths directed toward the root of the veins, and in the other direction are closed. Viewed from the outside they present an appearance not unlike the swellings which are seen in the branches and stem of a plant. In my opinion they are formed by nature in order that they may to a certain extent delay the blood and so prevent the whole of it from flowing at once like a flood either to the feet, or to the hands and fingers, and becoming collected there."

It should be repeated that Canano and not Fabrizio had discovered the valves in the veins. Fabrizio was the first to describe them publicly but unable to take his significant observations a creative step forward, he failed to achieve any real understanding of their function. He did not, however, gain his information from Canano. Instead, his knowledge of the veins seems to have come from one of the most unusual figures of the Renaissance and, possibly, in all history—Fra Paolo Sarpi.

Unlike Leonardo da Vinci whom he resembled in the boundless sweep of his powers, Sarpi is little remembered. We can only surmise his enormous contributions to man's knowledge through their reflections in the acclaimed work of others.

Today, few know of Sarpi or have even heard of him. Yet in his time, Fabrizio called him medicine's "oracle of this century" and Galileo acclaimed him as "My father and my master" in astronomy, adding that in mathematics "No man in Europe surpasses him." In optics Sarpi's work opened the way to our present theories of sight. He dissected the eye and discovered the actions and functions of the iris in relation to light. He gave this data to his friend Fabrizio who taught it in his classes. He did not invent the telescope as has been alleged, but he did put it to practical use by mapping the moon.

Fra Paolo recognized none of the boundaries that so often limit man's knowledge and activities. His contributions were scientific, medical, philosophical, theological and political. He was one of the first great champions of the freedom of thought and conscience —and it was this more than anything else that brought him into collision with the authority of the Church.

Sarpi's political enemies called him "the terrible friar" and vainly loosed the power of the Inquisition upon him. It may well be that those powerful enemies who failed by various means to destroy his body later succeeded, in part at least, in obliterating the memory of his accomplishments.

Born in Venice on August 14, 1552, Sarpi was brilliant even in his youth. He spent four years studying mathematics and Oriental languages at Mantua. An advanced scholar at the age of thirteen, he joined the Servite Order. At twenty he was a professor of theology and canon law.

The Republic of Venice, attempting to clarify its powers, became engaged in a bitter controversy with Pope Paul V regarding the extent of papal authority over secular affairs. Fra Paolo, a champion of the then revolutionary doctrine of the separation of church and state, was appointed theological consultant by the Venetian government. Under his guidance, the Senate of Venice enacted a number of laws which restricted the power of the Church over non-religious affairs, and even sought to curb the activities of the Holy Inquisition.

During this controversy Fra Paolo was accused of a number of crimes. Among them were charges of being anti-ecclesiastic and of consorting with Protestants. Then, along with the Republic of Venice, he was excommunicated and his writings were placed on the *Index Expurgatorius.*

During all this time Fra Paolo's interests ranged widely and probed deeply. Many fields of knowledge were enriched by his efforts. His most remarkable discoveries seem to have been made in his exploration of the circulation. He certainly studied the valves of the veins and knew their functions. This was information he gave to Fabrizio who then taught it to Harvey. There is also the fascinating possibility that the remarkable friar actually knew of the circulation of the blood.

Evidence for this exists in a letter written by Fra Paolo in which he refers to the book published by Vesalius. "Certain things in this work I have found with great pleasure because they seem analogous to those things already discovered and recorded by me regarding the circulation of the blood in the bodies of animals and the structure and use of their valves." The use of the word "circulation" is what is so important here since it described a concept that was still to be proposed.

Since his controversy with Rome continued unabated, the publication of Fra Paolo's writings was all but impossible throughout the Catholic world. Several times "the terrible friar" was asked to recant his views regarding freedom of thought and the separation of church and state. He refused, standing firm under the protection of the Venetian Republic. On the night of October 5, 1607, a band of assassins waylaid him and left him for dead. But Fra Paolo survived the knives and, it is recorded, even jested with his surgeon about the ragged nature of the wounds. As soon as he recovered he returned to his varied works and studies.

Apart from his scientific achievements the quality of this not-so-terrible friar's belief in the freedom of the human spirit can be gleaned from a prophetic note that he wrote upon hearing that Galileo had been called to Rome for questioning:

"I hear that Master Galileo is transferring himself to Rome, invited there by various Cardinals to show his discoveries in the heavens. I fear that if in such circumstances he brings before them the wise reasons which have led him to support the theory of Copernicus concerning our solar system, he will not fall in with the genius of the Jesuits and of other friars.

"The physical and astronomical question will be changed into a theological one, and I foresee to my great displeasure that to live in peace and without the mark of heresy and excommunication he will have to retract his statements on the subject.

"The day will come, however, of this I am nearly certain, that men illuminated by greater studies will deplore the misfortune of Galileo and the injustice used against so great a man. In the meantime he will have to suffer and lament himself, but in secret."

When Fra Paolo died in 1623, the bulk of his manuscripts were still unpublished. And most of them remained unpublished, stored in the library of the Servitian monastery to which he belonged. Then, in September 1769, a mysterious fire completely destroyed the library and the priceless manuscripts it contained. Of Fra Paolo's record of incredible intellectual achievement, only a few documents, some contemporary references and a mound of ashes remained.

Whether Fra Paolo did or did not himself discover the circulation of the blood is a fruitless question and not particularly pertinent. His contributions to Fabrizio concerning the valves certainly had their effect upon the work of Harvey and others. The description of the circulatory valves was available. The lesser circulation had already been defined. The fact that the arteries as well as the veins carried the blood was at last accepted and understood. And man's mind, shaking free from many of its fetters, was ready to open a new gateway into the future.

After all the millennia through which they had been found and lost over and over again, the theories that had once been advanced by the Chinese and Egyptians at last found a historical time in which man was not only receptive to them, but also possessed the means to accept and prove them.

So we come to the discovery of the circulation.

Chapter Thirteen

The Discoverers of the Circulation

In Europe, monuments have been erected to four men, honoring each of them as the discoverer of the circulation of the blood.

In Madrid, there is a monument to Miguel Servetus, the discoverer of the circulation.

In Bologna, there is a monument to Carlo Ruini, the discoverer of the circulation.

In Pisa, there is a monument to Andrea Cesalpino, the discoverer of the circulation.

In England there are several monuments to William Harvey, the discoverer of the circulation.

This completes the roll of monuments but not the distinguished list of discoverers. In France it has been claimed that the circulation was discovered by François Rabelais, who is less well remembered as a physician and surgeon than as an author.

There are some who credit the remarkable Fra Paolo Sarpi who did considerable work on the circulation and may indeed have traced its course. Then there are those who hold that it was Leonardo who first showed a full understanding of the circulation.

This still does not exhaust the list of notable claimants. The Arabs, with some justice, might name Ibn an-Nafis as the discoverer of the circulation, the Alexandrians might insist it was Erasistratus, and the Chinese certainly have legitimate reason to declare for the Emperor Hwang-ti.

Out of this still incomplete catalogue of claims, one simple conclusion emerges: The discovery of the circulation could not possibly have been the product of any one man's genius. Beginning with the primitive hunter who first saw blood spurting from a severed artery, the mapping of the river of life has been the work of many men from many nations spanning many ages, and those credited with the ultimate discovery are more accurately the harvesters of a widely scattered crop sown by a multitude of husbandmen.

Man and his communities, be they tribes or nations, tend to compete for recognition. Out of this human characteristic was born the great controversy over who actually "discovered" the circulation of the blood. Many candidates had their ardent advocates but the argument resolved itself mainly around the figures of Andrea Cesalpino and William Harvey.

What distinguished the work of these two was the fact that they not only described the circulation but they also demonstrated it. This was the key to their achievement. Where others may have guessed, theorized, developed brilliant hypotheses or actually performed experiments which were lost to history, Cesalpino and Harvey gathered the relevant facts and provided the scientific proof of the circulation.

The dispute that has raged over which single individual deserves the credit is more a matter of emotion than of scientific or historic necessity. Let it be said that in countries influenced by Anglo-Saxon culture, Harvey won out. Unquestionably, by providing the exact proof of almost each stage of the circulation he made a massive contribution to man's knowledge.

In Mediterranean areas Cesalpino tends to displace Harvey. His work—out of which Harvey's achievement flowed—was no less vital to the final mapping of the river of life and should neither be diminished nor denied.

Cesalpino, who preceded Harvey by some sixty years, was a product of the best of his times. Born in the Tuscan village of Arezzo on June 6, 1519, he recognized no narrow bounds of interest or specialty. He was a physician, a botanist, a mineralogist and a philosopher—winning great distinction in each of those fields. Cesalpino is credited with creating the first scientific approach to mineralogy. In botany, where he was the first to distinguish the sex of plants and to compare seeds with eggs, he has been called the first true systematist.

Whichever field of learning he entered, Cesalpino brought with him a cool, deliberate approach and a very precise methodology. He was never content to dash ahead with great éclat and flair toward some sweeping conclusion. Instead he moved slowly and with extreme care, testing each step before attempting the next. Cesalpino could accept neither Galen nor any other ancient master without first testing their teachings and confirming them to his own satisfaction. This attitude brought him great renown during his lifetime and ushered him to the brink of anathema and oblivion.

After studying at Padua under Vesalius he was appointed professor at the University of Pisa where he taught medicine, anatomy, botany and philosophy for many years, taking time out whenever possible for a number of botanical explorations through Italy. Cesalpino was a venerable scholar of 73 when, in 1592, he was called to Rome to become physician to Pope Clement VIII, and professor of medicine at the Roman center of learning, the Sapienza. There he remained until his death in 1603.

Cesalpino's contributions to mankind's intellectual wealth are contained in three books. The first, *Peripatetic Questions*, was published in Florence in 1569. Here Cesalpino described his theory of the circulation, showing among other things, that the heart and not the liver—as Galen had claimed—was the circulatory center. The second book, *De Plantis*, was published in 1583 and, although mainly a work on botany, Cesalpino used it to elaborate his theories of the circulation. In his final book, *Medical Questions*, published in 1593, the year after he came to Rome, he offered experimental proof of the total circulation described in his earlier works.

The picture of the circulation as provided by Cesalpino was virtually complete. He declared that there was a constant motion of blood from the veins to the right side of the heart. Then the blood flowed from the heart to the lungs, thence to the left side of the heart which sent the blood to all parts of the body through the arteries. These arteries he recognized as pulsating vessels through which the blood flowed at relatively high pressures.

From the arteries the blood passed through tiny "hair-like" vessels, which Cesalpino called "capillaries," into the veins which, he noted, did not pulsate and within which the blood flowed at a much lower pressure. The veins returned the blood to the heart to repeat the cycle over and over. This was the full circulation, completely described after all the millennia of exploration.

What made Cesalpino's description of the circulation so important was the fact that Cesalpino not only visualized the existence of capillaries which he could not possibly see, but that he actually demonstrated that such connecting vessels between the arteries and veins had to exist.

He exposed the vein of a living animal, tied it to stop the flow of blood, then made an incision between the ligature and where he believed the capillaries to exist. The blood which first flowed through this cut was dark and obviously venous. Then, as the flow continued, it became brighter in color and took on the appearance of arterial blood.

How could arterial blood flow into the veins unless there was some direct linkage, Cesalpino reasoned. Obviously the arteries were connected to the veins by vessels which became progressively smaller until they were like invisible hairs.

Cesalpino used a similar experiment to show the direction in which the blood flowed. At that time, it was generally believed that the blood flowed out of the heart into the veins rather than into the arteries. Cesalpino demonstrated experimentally that the reverse was true.

Since the blood flowed in one direction, he reasoned, this direction of flow could be determined by tying a vessel. The vessel would then swell on the side of the ligature from which the flow of blood came. In principle this was the same as damming a stream, with the water rising on the side of the dam from which the stream flowed.

The experiment clearly showed that the blood in the veins flowed toward the heart, not away from it.

In addition to mapping the general flow of the circulation and demonstrating the existence of the capillaries, Cesalpino went on to show that the blood was aerated in the lungs through tiny, branching vessels that came in close proximity to vessels containing air, rather than by direct contact as Galen had held.

Other explorers before Cesalpino had courageously contradicted Galen's view of the circulation and many of them had suffered for it. But Cesalpino offered a substantial body of experimental proof to substantiate his theories. Nevertheless, he came under fire from all sides even after his death. His philosophical writings alienated Protestant philosophers and his freedom of thought and disregard of dogma drew the ire of many Catholic authorities. After all, the whole Galenic view of the various spirits which constituted the soul was demolished by Cesalpino's demonstration of the circulation.

As the controversy over credit developed, some of the disputants claimed that Cesalpino had contributed nothing; or, if he did, he either did not fully understand his own theories or did not prove them. But the precise evidence of his achievement lives in his three books. Yet Cesalpino's work, invaluable though it was, did not create a new era in medicine, anatomy and physiology as did Harvey's.

Certainly neither man actually "discovered" the circulation but both of them made massive contributions to its full understanding and experimental proof. Yet men, whether they be enlightened scientists or primitive witch doctors, seem to share a common urge to seize the spotlight for themselves, either directly or indirectly through some cult hero with whom they identify.

Just as Cesalpino was ignored and his accomplishments belittled or denied by supporters of Galen and proponents of Harvey, Harvey was attacked by the Galenic dogmatists as well as by advocates of Cesalpino and earlier explorers. The Englishman was even stigmatized as an "intellectual pirate" by the 19th-century Italian physiologist, Ceradini.

William Harvey, the man who brought an end to the primitive era of exploration of the river of life, was born in Folkstone, England, on April 1, 1578. Intellectually he was an Italian of the Renaissance. After studying at Cambridge, he was inevitably drawn to the renowned University of Padua where he became the favorite student of Fabrizio d'Aquapendente.

A man of insatiable intellectual appetites, Harvey was an omnivorous reader. He certainly knew of Cesalpino's work which had been published in its entirety when he came to Padua. He also had available the work of Ruini, Colombo and of Fra Paolo Sarpi, the friend of his teacher. He must also have known something, at least, of Servetus. Harvey received his degree at Padua in 1602 and he returned to England. He became physician to James I and his son Charles I.

In London, with the spell of Padua and the Renaissance still upon him, Harvey began the series of experiments that won him immortality. Twenty years of dedicated effort were poured into this carefully designed task to demonstrate the mechanics of the circulation. The result of all this labor, reduced to its essence, was published in Frankfort, Germany, in 1628. Entitled *De Motu Cordis*, this concise 72-page book became the key to an utterly new concept of anatomy and physiology.

Harvey united the Italian tradition of anatomy with the other experimental sciences that were emerging in Europe. He was not content merely to describe the results of his dissections. Instead he probed into the mechanics and purposes of the processes that his experiments revealed. Mathematics, mechanics and hydraulics were as much his tools as scalpels, clamps and ligatures.

His mathematical proof of the circulation was a marvel of clarity and simplicity. He showed that each time the heart contracted it ejected two fluid ounces of blood. In the course of an hour, therefore, the heart beating an average of 72 times a minute pumps out

8,640 fluid ounces of blood. Since the weight of this blood would be three times greater than the total weight of an average human being, there was but one explanation for the apparent contradiction. The body must contain a limited amount of blood which the heart pumps over and over again through a fixed circulatory system.

"It is absolutely necessary to conclude," wrote Harvey, "that the blood in the animal body is impelled in a circle and is in a state of ceaseless motion, that this is the act or function which the heart performs by means of its pulses; and that it is the sole and only end of the motion and contraction of the heart."

From this starting point, Harvey went through the entire circulation, describing what happened and showing the mechanics of how it happened each step of the way. There was only one great omission in his work. Harvey failed to visualize the capillaries and include them in his picture of the circulation. Instead of the hair-like vessels Cesalpino had described as connecting the arteries with the veins, Harvey thought that the blood passed from the arteries to the veins through "porosities in the flesh."

Taking this single oversight into account, we find that Harvey actually described two half-circulations rather than a complete circulation. The capillary linkage, although it was assumed by Cesalpino, had to await the use of the microscope before it could actually be revealed.

Harvey's book, of course, aroused a storm of controversy. Galen's supporters were furious. Many of these traditionalists, the medical and scientific leaders of the time, believed Harvey's doctrine of the circulation to be so revolutionary that it might overthrow medicine itself—at least as it was then being practiced and taught. All means seemed justified to prevent this catastrophe. The battle cry that resounded through the world of medicine seemed to be: "Better Galen's errors than Harvey's truths!"

Harvey was assailed by some of the most distinguished leaders of European medicine. Among these were the German physician Caspar Hoffmann, and the Frenchman Jean Riolan who, upon

Fabrizio's death, was considered to be the foremost anatomist of his time. Later detractors of Harvey, such as Ceradini, the 19th-century professor of physiology at the University of Genoa, maintained that "Harvey owed his success to the opposition of the Parisian anatomist . . . had Cesalpino during his life met with a Riolan to accuse him of plagiarism, absurdity and heresy . . . no one could have taken from him the great renown of his discovery."

Most of the later attack on Harvey deals with his failure to mention the work of his contemporaries and predecessors who had cleared the path he followed.

The issues involved here are delicate and subject to various interpretations. We must recognize that all the explorers of the river of life ventured onto dangerous ground. The Inquisition was a constant threat to free thought, and those who had come under its critical eye were avoided by those who feared that guilt might be held contagious. Guilt by association is a phenomenon we have seen even in our own times. Under those circumstances it was dangerous to avow an association, even in thought, with those who were stigmatized by the charge of heresy. Considerations of ethics, morality and personal courage sometimes appear to take on great flexibility when subjected to the erosion of fear.

The intellectual climate of Harvey's England was clouded with the same fears as the rest of Europe. In the conflicts that resulted in the beheading of Charles I by Cromwell, free thought and expression were frequently fatal. It might be noted that even in 1628, Harvey did not publish his book in his native England but sought a printer in Germany. After the restoration of the monarchy, still severer restrictions on thought and belief were imposed. Heretics were banished and even quiet prayer meetings, held in private, were considered treasonable.

The curbs were so great, wrote John C. Hemmeter, the noted American physiologist and medical historian in his study of the discovery of the circulation, that even twenty years after Harvey's death "nobody could venture publicly to adhere to Cesalpino and

Servetus. No wonder, therefore, that Harvey does not mention Cesalpino and Servetus, even had he known them by heart."

When Harvey died in 1657, the river of life had finally been mapped in all but one of its major aspects. Justified at last were Atothis, Imhotep, Emperor Hwang-ti and Erasistratus. The seeds they had scattered had borne fruit.

The distortions and the dogmas were laid to rest. The blood flowed in a circle. Pumped by the muscular heart, it passed through the arteries into the body and back through the veins to the heart. From there it was sent to the lungs for aeration, then back to the heart and out once more through the arteries.

This was the scheme of the circulation—no longer mere speculation or theory but demonstrable fact.

The belief in the pneuma that purportedly flowed through the arteries was demolished. The pulsating arteries, carrying blood under pressure, had no room for the mystic soul.

This was a river that obeyed the laws of mechanics rather than magic. The operation of the heart pump and the directional function of the valves were expressions of mechanical laws, the varying pressures within the arteries and veins followed the laws of hydraulics. The river of life flowed through caverns measurable to man.

Only one gap remained to be filled before the broad map of the river could be considered complete. That was the physical discovery of the capillaries.

Chapter Fourteen

Malpighi and the Microscope Reveal the Capillaries

Of the unnumbered creatures that evolved out of the primal sea, man alone has made such prolific use of tools to extend his powers that, in virtually every respect, he has become at once one of the most puissant and most dependent of all living things.

Man uses tools—a house, clothing, heat, air conditioning—to help him cope with climate. He uses tools to gather and prepare food. Primitive man, who could not outrun the antelope, could kill it with swift arrows; and his spear gave him a longer and sharper tooth than the tiger.

Man is protected, sheltered and strengthened by tools. He can cross the sea more quickly than any fish, fly faster and higher than any bird and on land he can easily outstrip the speediest hunting leopard. Merely by pushing a button he can command a strength incomparably greater than that of all the whales in all the oceans. From his birth to his death modern man is supported by his tools. The bed on which he sleeps, the clock that measures his time, the stove at which he cooks, the plate off which he eats, the desk at which he works, the telephone that extends the range of his voice, the chemical and biological substances that help him ward off illness and pain, his eyeglasses, handkerchief, bridgework and golf clubs—all these are only a fraction of the tools man uses almost as naturally and unthinkingly as he uses his lungs to breathe. He has become so adapted to them that he hardly considers them tools at all, but extensions of himself.

There is some dispute over whether man has become so dependent on tools that they may ultimately destroy him. But there can be little question that without tools and the intelligence that created them, man would have been long extinct.

When man made the telescope he increased the power of his eyes to explore in detail the further reaches of space. Then, to see into the world of the invisibly small, he produced the microscope.

As far back as Alexandrian days, a few men had used water-filled globes to provide low-powered but distorted magnification. The concept of the microscope probably existed then, but the technology of the times was not equipped to produce an effective instrument.

The exact inventor of the microscope is not known. The first one was probably built about 1590 by Zacharias Janssen, a lens grinder of Middelburg. Galileo and others have at various times been credited with the discovery, but the available evidence points to the Dutch lens maker.

To a large extent the microscope was almost statistically inevitable at the time. There was a growing need for such a tool, the techniques needed to produce it were well developed and there was a large supply of available lenses. What was needed was the right combination of existing circumstances.

At first the microscope was little more than a scientific novelty of great fascination. For several decades after its invention it was considered a sort of toy that could stimulate the imagination. It was only after the capabilities of this new instrument were sufficiently tested that it came into use in specific experiments in anatomy, physiology, biology and other sciences.

The anatomists of the Renaissance had done a most effective job solely with the unaided eye. But by the time Harvey had completed his work, the human eye had approached its limits. Man had probed as deeply as he could into the study of the body. He could already see most of the organs in their overall form, but the refinements and the exquisite details of these structures and tissues remained invisible. To go further he needed a new instrument which could extend his limited vision.

Galileo broke through the barrier. If he did not actually build the first microscope he was undoubtedly the first to use it scientifically. He made his first instrument in 1610 by adapting a telescope he was already using. Fascinated by the possibilities that were revealed, he constructed an improved microscope and began a systematic study of insects, plants and other living things, making detailed records of what he saw.

A new world was revealed. For the first time man saw creatures living and dying in a microscopic universe the very existence of which was almost impossible to imagine. He observed the cells out of which living tissue was built. He studied the organs of insects. Finally, he recognized that the tiny universe formed the material out of which man's larger universe was constructed.

The effect of the microscope was revolutionary. Scientists suddenly found themselves asking questions they had never dreamed of before; and the experiments in which they framed those questions produced some astonishing answers.

The blood was shown to be something other than the red fluid man had believed it to be. The flesh was revealed as much more complex than the visible mass of fibrous tissue. And the capillaries necessary to complete man's map of the circulation were magnified from the realm of theoretical speculation to the world of visible reality.

The concluding step in the mapping of the river of life was taken by Marcello Malpighi, another of Italy's superbly creative scientists. Born near Bologna in 1628, the year Harvey published his book, Malpighi's fertile talents enriched the sciences of entomology, zoology and botany as well as anatomy and experimental medicine.

Malpighi was one of the first to use the microscope in biological research, and his studies of the minute structures of tissues were the basis of a new science called histology. His microscopic explorations ranged from the organs of silkworms to those of eagles.

His investigations of the tissues of animals, insects and plants were the most profound of his time.

So great was the sweep of his curiosity that the discovery of the capillaries came seemingly as a matter of course. The year was 1661, almost two thousand years after Erasistratus had postulated their existence and some sixty-eight years after Cesalpino had named them in his final book.

Malpighi was examining the lung of a frog. Viewed through the naked eye it appeared to be little more than a mass of membranous sacs. But the microscope revealed a complex structure of tissues, cells and vessels. Some of the frog's blood had remained in a minute section of the lung Malpighi was examining. His description of what he saw was the final step in the mapping of the circulation.

"To a marked extent there was preserved the redness of the blood in very minute traps . . . where by the help of a glass [i.e. microscope] I saw not scattered points, but vessels joined together in a ring-like fashion.

"And such is the wandering about of these vessels as they proceed on one side from the vein and on the other from the artery that they no longer maintain a straight direction, but seem to become a network . . . [between] . . . the two vessels."

It was a moment charged with such drama and triumph that Malpighi was moved to declare: "It has happened to me to see such things that, not undeserving, I might in the present situation use the saying of Homer: 'I see with my eyes a sure great work.' "

With the existence of the capillaries proved, Malpighi and a number of contemporaries set out to learn if they existed in warm-blooded animals as well as in reptiles. With the science and techniques of microscopy still barely developed, this posed insurmountable problems at the time, and it was more than a century before Malpighi's discovery was confirmed in warm-blooded creatures.

The physiologist Lazzaro Spallanzani accomplished it in the spring of 1771. He turned his microscope on a hen's egg containing a developing chick. He might have failed had he not realized that the viewing required more than the inadequate lighting available in his laboratory.

"Since the room in which I worked did not have a sufficient light," wrote Spallanzani, "and I was determined in some way to satisfy my curiosity, I resolved to examine the egg in the open air, by direct sunlight . . . I immediately focused the lens upon it and, in spite of the flood of light which surrounded me, I could, by partially closing my eyes, distinctly see the blood circulate through the entire complex of the arterial and venous umbilical vessels. Overcome by this unexpected pleasure, I felt at liberty now to cry out: 'I have found it, I have found it!' "

The course of the river of life was now completely traced and fully mapped, at least in its broad aspects. Many areas still remained to be understood and elaborated. The manner in which the blood was aerated was not yet clearly known. Nor did man know how the products of digestion entered the blood stream to be transported to the various parts of the body. This and more still waited to be discovered. But the first realm of knowledge—that of the circulation—was no longer in shadow.

The task of exploring the nature of the blood, its composition and its functions, yet remained. It had been obvious, as anyone with eyes could see, that the blood was a fluid, that it was red, that its color was brighter in arteries than in veins, that it clotted under certain circumstances and that it must have an important part in the life functions. Beyond that, virtually nothing was known although there existed a large number of strongly held and frequently conflicting beliefs. These were mainly concerned with the magical, mystical and spiritual properties of blood. As for the medical concepts of blood, they had not yet been freed of the absurdities which made bloodletting the treatment for almost all physical, emotional and spiritual ills. The nature of the blood was shrouded in such utter mystery that, had it not been for the microscope, man might not even have realized that it existed at all.

It was Malpighi, again, who discovered the first clue. Using his microscope to penetrate beyond the obvious, he showed that the blood was not a simple, red fluid and that the human eye had been deceived by its innate limitations. Then, in 1665, four years after he had discovered the capillaries, Malpighi discovered the red cells in the blood of man. With this a new world of exploration was opened.

The blood was now seen as the carrier of at least one normally invisible solid element, and possibly more which remained to be found and identified. In the balanced economy of nature these probably had specific functions which could only be determined by new knowledge, new tools, new techniques and new experiments.

More and more scientists, their curiosity stirred, rose to the challenge. The finding of the red cells led, ultimately, to the discovery of the respiratory function of the blood. The finding of one solid element in the blood led to the search for others and the discovery of the leukocytes—the white cells—and various other formed elements that are a part of the substance of the river of life.

And all of this was unlocked by Malpighi and his microscope.

Once more, as at all other crossroads of human development, man divided against himself. One part, small but bold, sought to press forward. The other part, larger, powerful and entrenched, resisted change because it seemed to threaten their established positions. Between these extremes, the bulk of mankind, pulled ahead by one part of itself and dragged back by the other, managed to move slowly if painfully forward.

In Malpighi's native city of Bologna where he came to publish his findings and where he founded a new school of anatomy, students who were anxious to explore the newly illuminated paths gathered around him. But many of the securely established physicians and scientists met him with fierce hostility. Malpighi, they correctly feared, threatened to upset the beliefs upon which their positions rested. Galen's dogma still had numerous and potent adherents who doggedly resisted the introduction of any new truth that might further erode their crumbling fortress of faith.

The fact that Malpighi could provide the evidence of microscopic observation only made him more dangerous and threatening. It had been much the same with the anatomical evidence provided by Servetus, Cesalpino and Harvey. The bitterness against Malpighi grew. He was attacked on all sides; ridiculed, slandered and publicly derided. Articles were written denouncing him. Beset by adversity and wretchedly unhappy, Malpighi worked on, a solitary titan charting the microscopic regions of life.

Then some colleagues from the University of Bologna decided on direct action. Covering their faces with masks, they beat Malpighi brutally, and sacked his house, burning many of his papers and destroying his laboratory. But both the microscope and Malpighi's findings persisted and continued to open new doorways to knowledge. Malpighi, too, managed to survive the assault and spent his final years in Rome as physician to Pope Innocent XI.

Barely a moment after Malpighi in time, another pioneer, Anton von Leeuwenhoek, surged forward on an almost identical course. This astonishing Netherlander built a microscope after grinding his own lenses. There were many unusual aspects to this multi-faceted man. First of all, he was a dry-goods clerk turned scholar. He had never been to university and had studied neither Latin, Greek nor any of the classics. Yet, entirely self-taught, with a wealth of natural ability and a profound love of science, he became one of the world's most creative microscopists.

Leeuwenhoek, like Malpighi, did not use the microscope as a toy, or a passport into a novel wonderland. Instead he recognized it as a serious instrument that had to be used with strict discipline. In 1673, eight years after Malpighi had first seen red cells in the blood of man, Leeuwenhoek found similar red cells in the blood of animals. With this find it was now apparent that the red cells were no magical substances that made man unique among living things. Rather the cells were a normal physical constituent of blood, regardless of the being in which it flowed.

Meticulous in his experiments, the Dutch scientist attempted to measure the size of the red cell and describe its physical structure. His results were remarkably close to being accurate. Considering that the red cell is about $3/10{,}000$ of an inch in diameter and $1/10{,}000$ of an inch thick, one marvels at the quality of the work being undertaken in those early days when the microscope was still in a primitive form.

Leeuwenhoek studied the walls of the blood vessels that controlled the movement of the blood, and set up experiments to measure the velocity of the blood flow. He was also the first to see bacteria and recognize them as distinct organisms. His drawing of these strange creatures appeared in 1683 in the British scientific journal known as *Philosophical Transactions.* This was man's first view of the microbes—those previously invisible and unknown neighbors with which he shares the world.

As more and more scientists began to use the microscope, understanding and techniques improved. Data and experience accumulated as each new answer stimulated new questions and new experiments.

As far back as Alexandrian and Greek times, anatomists had occasionally come upon vessels, often thought to be nerves, which contained a yellow or whitish fluid. Such vessels had been seen and described by Erasistratus who had the misfortune of being several thousand years ahead of his time.

A professor of Padua, Gaspare Aselli by name, rediscovered these vessels on July 23, 1622, while performing an autopsy on a dog in the presence of some friends. Noticing certain whitish cords in the abdomen, he thought at first that they were nerves. Then, quickly realizing that the nerves of the intestine, where these cords were located, were quite different, he cut across one of them, releasing a whitish fluid. His delight was so great that he turned to his friends and shouted, "Eureka! I have found it!"

Actually he did not quite know what he found. Because of the milk-like color of the fluid, he called them lacteal vessels. He imagined that they carried the products of digestion to the liver where they were supposedly converted into blood. As it turned out, none of this was true.

About a quarter of a century later, in 1648, a young physician of Dieppe named Jean Pecquet was doing advanced work at the University of Montpelier and discovered that these vessels did not empty their contents into the liver at all. Instead they led into the duct of the thorax which, in turn, emptied into the *vena cava,* the great vein that brought the blood back into the heart.

Two years later a Swedish medical student at the University of Padua, Olaf Rudbeck, found similar vessels in the liver which also emptied their contents into the thoracic duct and, ultimately into the *vena cava.*

The parts of the puzzle were put together in 1652 by the Danish anatomist Thomas Bartholin. He found such vessels in all parts of the body and noticed that all of them ultimately sent their contents into a confluence with the blood. So developed the work that was to define and delineate the lymphatic circulation which, though a side stream, is a part of the total flow of the river of life. The lymph, which consists of a fluid portion of the blood which passes through the capillary walls to the cells, bathes the tissues just as the original mother sea bathed the surfaces of the first living organisms. It then flows off to be gathered by vessels of its own and ultimately returned into the blood from which it came.

The tendency of man's growing knowledge has been to reveal the complexity of the universe rather than reduce it to simplicity. Primitive man was able to describe his universe and its forces in the simplest of terms. There were good demons and bad demons, white magic and black. Today we see a universe so complex that ordinary language, sophisticated as it has become, can no longer describe many of its phenomena. Space-time continua, for instance, cannot even be visualized, let alone described in other than symbolic terms.

Similarly, the mapping of the circulation did not bring an end to the exploration of the river of life or reduce its complexities to simplicities. Instead it revealed previously unknown areas and posed more intricate problems.

Chapter Fifteen

Light Spreads Along the River

Europe entered a period of explosive growth as it passed out of the Renaissance and moved toward the Industrial Revolution. As the thin but rigid crust of feudalism began to crack under the pressure of the emerging middle class, the whole structure of society shifted and readjusted, unlocking a new potential of human energy and creativity.

The expansion of manufacturing and trade brought a growing demand for better tools and techniques, faster transportation, improved communication. Science responded to the needs of the times, searching out the secrets of nature and turning them to the advantage of man.

Astronomy brought more accurate navigation. Physics, mathematics, chemistry and the other branches of knowledge brought better looms, more useful metals, more efficient power sources, more permanent dyes for the textile industry, faster ships and so on.

The accelerating accumulation of new knowledge in its turn created new needs, and so both need and knowledge followed each other in ascending, expanding spirals.

As the fever of scientific discovery and exploration spread, interest and excitement seemed to percolate through the levels of society. The wonders and marvels revealed by science became topics of common discussion. A butcher or a baker might have pertinent comments about the latest controversy over the circulation or the place of the sun in the universe. As communication improved, men became better able to exchange ideas, arguments, doubts and criticisms.

Inevitably, scientists and scholars gathered into associations and societies that permitted a more direct exchange. They held meetings, reported on their work, described their findings and their problems, put forward new and challenging ideas. Soon even the small towns of Europe had their societies where views could be aired and opinions exchanged by laymen, scholars, and occasional charlatans.

In London a group of enlightened young men, amateur scientists as well as non-conformists of their time, gathered in coffee shops and taverns to discuss the latest discoveries and to advance their own theories. In 1645 they organized themselves into what became known as the "Invisible College." Because of various pressures and misunderstandings, they moved to Oxford, where free discussion survived with relative security. Gradually the group gained considerable support. In 1662, after the English Civil War had ended, Charles II chartered them as the Royal Society of London.

The purpose of the group, according to its first historian Thomas Sprat, ". . . was no more, than only the satisfaction of breathing a freer air, and of conversing in quiet with one another, without being ingag'd in the passions and madness of that dismal Age . . . to make faithful records of all the works of nature, or art which can come within their reach . . ."

As for science, Sprat wrote that the Society's members ". . . have attempted to free it from the artifice, and humors, and passions of sects; to render it an instrument whereby mankind may obtain a dominion over Things, and not only over one another's judgements."

Two years after receiving its royal charter, the Society began to publish its *Philosophical Transactions*, one of the world's first and best known scientific journals, which, incidentally, is still published today. It was here that Malpighi's work was reported and where Leeuwenhoek's drawings of bacteria first appeared.

Similar societies emerged in Italy, Germany and other countries. The French Academy which had been founded by Cardinal Richelieu in 1653, evolved into the French Academy of Sciences and began to publish its transactions in 1699.

The societies and their journals brought increasing vigor to the interchange of ideas. A discovery in one country was quickly reported to the scientists of other countries. Malpighi, for instance, was far better known and more highly respected in England, France and Germany than he was in his own city of Bologna. Harvey's discoveries were known in England, France, Germany and Italy almost simultaneously, and they were discussed in lively fashion throughout Europe's scientific circles.

Ironically, some of the same academies and societies that helped liberate science later became instruments of restriction and dogma themselves. As centers of scientific authority, they tended to acquire the inertia of respectability, and the resulting atrophy sometimes led them to resist the disturbing onslaught of fresh ideas. Today, the very term "academic" carries the implication of rigid formalism and conformity to tradition. But in their youthful vigor, these societies helped provide driving force and direction to the scientific revolution that was to change—and is still changing—the face of the world.

Within man the blood coursed on. But its chemical composition, how and where it was formed, its purposes and the mechanisms of its activities were still unknown. As for the manner in which the blood supplied the body tissues with the oxygen necessary to all life functions, that was a puzzle hidden in a mystery, since the very existence of oxygen was still to be discovered.

Oddly, the discovery of the respiratory function of the blood really began with the invention of the air pump, which made it possible to create a vacuum. Using this absence of air as a laboratory tool, it was possible to devise experiments that tested the effect of air, and its absence, on living matter.

One of the first contributions toward an understanding of the effect of air was made by the Italian physiologist Spallanzani, who had discovered the capillaries in warmblooded animals. Spallanzani's contemporaries believed that air was necessary to the circulation and that an animal deprived of air died because the circulation stopped. Spallanzani was able to produce evidence that this was false. The circulation did not stop in the absence of air. Instead, he maintained, the animal died because the lack of air produced some damage to the nervous system.

In the 18th century, the whole matter of air was as obscure as the blood had once been. Man's knowledge of it consisted mainly of weird fancies. Paracelsus had named air with the Greek word *chaos*. Out of the concept this conveyed, the word "gas" was later derived.

The science of chemistry, newly emerging out of alchemy, finally penetrated the mystery of the air. Chemistry probably originated in ancient China out of attempts to extract a magical substitute for blood from the red mineral called cinnebar. Now, chemical studies into the nature of air revealed a number of startling facts. For one thing, air was not a single gas as had long been believed, but a combination of gases each with a different property.

Oxygen had already been produced by a chemist named Borch in 1678, but he did not know what it was or even that it was a component of air. Carbon dioxide was discovered in 1755 by Joseph Black who, although he learned some of its properties, did not clearly identify it.

Then a most unusual German appeared to liven up the scene. This was Otto von Guericke, Mayor of Magdeburg. A showman of no modest proportions, von Guericke spent huge sums of money on experiments designed to create a vacuum. After building an effective air pump, he joined two hemispheric vessels and removed the air they contained. Then, amid a festive and circus-like atmosphere, he performed a spectacular experiment. In the presence of the Emperor and his entire court he demonstrated the amazing power of emptiness—the vacuum—by showing that sixteen horses were required on each side to pull the vessels apart.

In the latter part of the 17th century the vacuum became an important tool in the investigation of the properties of air. Two members of the Royal Society of London, the Irish chemist Robert Boyle and his assistant Robert Hooke, performed a series of experiments which showed that neither life nor burning could continue in a vacuum. As they removed the air from a container, living things within it died, and well-fueled fires went out. Obviously there was something in air that was essential to both combustion and life.

Boyle and Hooke came very close to discovering oxygen and its importance in the life processes. Actually, Boyle even decided that it was a component of the air, rather than the whole air itself, that was essential to burning and which turned arterial blood red. He called this mysterious element of air the "little vital quintessence."

With the still limited techniques and scientific theory available to them, Boyle and Hooke went about as far as they could. The isolation of oxygen and the understanding of the respiratory function of the blood awaited new knowledge and new experience. This was not long in coming.

It was an age of titans. Newton, Galileo, Boyle, Malpighi, Hooke, Harvey, Leeuwenhoek and many other giants worked within the span of less than a century. Information, experimental evidence and theoretical possibilities accumulated; tools and techniques improved and were refined; previously unsuspected laws of nature were rapidly revealed and took on new clarity; new gateways to understanding were opened.

In 1774 John Priestley, an English chemist, produced oxygen by heating the red oxide of mercury. Then, in a series of well-planned experiments, he demonstrated that this gas was the portion of the air that was used up in breathing as well as in burning. Priestley further showed that in sunlight green plants actually extracted oxygen from the carbon dioxide they absorbed. The sequence of discovery that followed led to the unraveling of the carbon cycle whereby nature achieves a balanced economy: animals take oxygen from the air and return carbon dioxide, and plants take carbon dioxide and return oxygen. Through his progression of probings, Priestley brought into the reach of human understanding the chemical nature of the life processes.

This was a shattering concept. Many men, confronted with the new realities of science, found it painfully difficult, if not impossible, to shed the deeply ingrained beliefs of the past.

Compromises were made. The soul, or vital spirit, which had previously been thought to flow through the arteries took on a newer, more generalized aspect. Some philosophers and physicians of the 18th century even found a place for the soul in these newly discovered chemical transformations. The chemistry of the human body, they declared, is unlike any other set of chemical processes because it is controlled by the soul.

Priestley's work was taken up and elaborated by the French scientist, Antoine Lavoisier, who died on the guillotine in 1794. Using more advanced techniques than those available to Priestley, he showed that the body acted in much the same way as a fire, burning the nutrients in its food and liberating heat and energy. The oxygen essential to this process came from the air and was distributed to the tissues by the blood.

With this, man penetrated another major area of the darkness that had obscured his understanding. The respiratory function of the blood, and its role in the chemistry of life was now accepted in its general outlines as a phenomenon that deserved closer study.

Much remained—and still remains—to be brought to light. But the pathways had been opened. The momentum had been achieved and was accelerating. The rest was a matter of time, effort, intelligence and motivation. The river of life lay open to man's ultimate explorations.

Part Five THE River We Know

Chapter Sixteen The Course of the River

The ancient sea flowed around each independent cell, feeding and bathing it and maintaining the environment within which it could survive. The blood has no such easy course.

Our blood must nourish, lave and provide for each of the hundreds of trillions of cells within the intricately organized structure that is the human body. To accomplish this the capillaries permeate every tissue, bringing the blood within reach of every cell. The ultimate purpose of the circulation—to bring the blood to the capillaries where it can fulfill its major tasks. The heart, arteries, veins and all the other structures, mechanisms and complex controls are primarily designed to achieve that end.

Not all the channels of the circulation carry blood at all times. There simply is not enough blood in the body for that. The microscopic capillaries alone could hold more than the body's total of about six quarts. What does happen in response to the needs of the body's economy is so magnificent that even the towering intricacies of a Bach fugue pale by comparison.

The blood, critically controlled by the vasomotor centers—a mesh of nerves in the primitive part of the brain known as the *medulla oblongata*—aided by message stations throughout the circulation and in other parts of the body, and stimulated or inhibited by hormones and other chemical substances, is precisely directed to those capillaries that require it. The operating rule is a simple one: blood is delivered according to the amount of work being done. Tissues doing heavy work receive a large supply of blood to provide for their energy needs and to remove the byproducts of work. Tissues at rest receive only enough blood to meet their minimal needs for healthy survival.

During sleep the body performs little work and most of the circulatory vessels are closed down. But if the bedcovers are inadvertantly tossed aside and the body is chilled, the capillaries of the skin suddenly receive an emergency supply of warming blood. If the body is ill or injured, the affected tissues require and receive considerable blood.

The most important work done by the body seems to be the digestion of food. According to the priority system set up for the blood, digestion takes precedence over ordinary muscular activity and even the most exalted thinking. After a meal the major part of the blood is directed to the digestive tract. To meet this increased need for blood, the brain and other tissues and muscles of the body are placed on short rations. This explains why we often feel drowsy and mentally sluggish after a meal; and why, if we undertake strenuous physical activity immediately after eating, the muscles may become cramped and quickly fatigued. For this reason we are warned against swimming soon after mealtime.

The traffic needs of the circulation are physically regulated by what might be considered a system of sluice gates at the openings of the vessels. Even the mouths of the tiniest capillaries have miniscule muscle fibers that contract to close the entrance if blood is not needed or relax to open it if there is a demand for blood. Along the more than 60,000 miles of the circulatory course, thousands upon thousands of tiny gateways and sluices are ceaselessly opening and closing, sending blood now here, now there, in a flow capable of so vast a number of possible combinations that, during an entire lifetime, no one pattern need ever be repeated.

Directions given to the circulatory system follow pathways so intricate that we do not yet fully understand them. Chemistry certainly plays an important part as do electrical impulses generated by chemical changes in the body tissues. We suspect that carbon dioxide, accumulating in the cells above a certain level, sets into motion a series of biochemical signal relays that results in the opening of the muscular sphincter at the mouth of the particular capillary supplying those cells.

At the same time, impulses so fast that they are almost instantaneous are sent through the nerve relays to the vasomotor center in the brain indicating a need for blood in that particular area. Immediate orders are sent through other nerve channels to the arterial muscles, directing them to so arrange the opening or closing of their gateways that sufficient blood will be sent to the area making the request.

Even from the relatively little we know of these mechanisms, it is clear that the flow of the blood is no haphazard tumbling of vital fluids along an unchanging course. Unlike the usual rivers which are open systems, beginning one place and ending someplace else, this strange river is a closed system that constantly returns to its source. Its total course, its channels and the direct mechanisms of its propulsion are known as the cardiovascular system. This includes the pumping heart which thrusts the blood out on its surging way; the arteries and their small branches, the arterioles, which carry the blood outward; the capillaries where the blood performs its destined function; then the venules and larger veins that carry the blood back to the heart.

Although the various vessels that carry the blood differ from one another, they all have one thing in common. All interior parts of the riverbed through which the blood flows—the vessels and the heart as well—are surfaced with a delicate lining of extremely thin cells laid end to end very much like a formation of paving blocks. These are known as *endothelial* cells, and the system which they form is called the *endothelium* or *endothelial system.* So thin are these cells that ten thousand of them, stacked one upon the other, would make a pile less than one inch high.

The arteries that carry the blood out into the system are tough, elastic tubes well supplied with muscle and nerve fibers. The arterial walls are constructed in three layers. The inner layer is the thin lining of endothelial cells. The middle layer, many times thicker than the endothelium, consists of smooth muscle and fibers of elastic connective tissue. The outer layer is made of loose connective tissue which carries small vessels to nourish the arterial wall, and nerve fibers to carry messages and direct the arterial muscles.

In the large arteries, such as the aorta which carries the full thrust of the driving blood from the heart, the proportion of elastic tissue in the middle layer is higher than that of muscle tissue. This gives the larger arteries the greater resiliency they need to take up the powerful thrust of the blood as it is driven out of the heart. As the arteries branch and become progressively smaller, the proportion of muscle tissue increases. The arterioles, the very smallest tubes of the arterial system, are mainly muscular. They have very little elastic tissue in their middle layer. These muscles make it possible for the arterioles, which serve as tiny faucets bringing blood to the capillaries, to contract or relax, thus shutting off or turning on the blood flow according to the directions of the body.

The capillary network or "bed" forms the largest part of the cardiovascular system and consists of the most delicate and fragile vessels of the body. Their walls have only one layer, a single smooth paving of endothelial cells no more than $1/10,000$ of an inch thick. Through the microscopic spaces between these cells the blood delivers its materials to the body tissues and picks up waste and other biochemical products. At the mouths of the capillaries, where they are joined to the arterioles by a sort of intermediary channel, there are rings of thin muscle fibers called sphincters. By relaxing or contracting, these open or close each capillary to the flow of blood.

At the other end of the capillary bed, the venous system begins with the venules and moves on to progressively larger veins until it reaches the *venae cavae,* the two large veins that return the blood into the heart.

The veins are constructed in much the same way as the arteries except that their walls are thinner and the diameter of their openings larger. Since they need not contract as do the arteries, they also contain less muscle fiber in the middle layer. Unlike the arteries, where pressure from the beating heart keeps the blood moving outward, the veins contain valves which permit the blood to flow only one way, back to the heart.

This, in most general terms, is how the channels of the circulation are constructed, each designed to meet with greatest efficiency the functional standards set by that least sentimental of all judges, natural selection.

No less unique than the circulatory vessels is that most unusual and most efficient of machines, the heart. This double-action pump performs its work by the alternate contraction and relaxation of powerful rings of muscle, thrusting some five quarts of blood through the system each minute, or 7,200 quarts every day.

During an average human lifetime of seventy years, the heart pumps almost 46 million gallons of blood through the body. Beating at the rate of 72 times a minute, it performs a total of more than 2.5 billion pumping strokes. Throughout this phenomenal working span, during which it has no rest other than the brief intervals between beats, the heart has no time out for repair, rehabilitation or replacement of parts as mechanical pumps have. Instead, the heart must continue working, mending its own damage and replacing worn-out tissues as it continues its ceaseless pumping.

The weight of this incredible machine is only about 11 ounces.

And its efficiency is greater by far than that of any man-made machine, regardless of size, using chemical fuels. The steam turbine, for instance, can convert about 25 percent of its fuel directly into work. The heart is twice as efficient, turning 50 percent of the nutrient and oxygen supplied it into work.

In addition to doing a great amount of work over a long period, the heart has another most unusual feature. It is self-regulating, adjusting its output to meet the needs of the body it serves. Ordinarily it may pump an average of five quarts a minute. But should the body do heavy work, say run a hundred yards at top speed, the heart may speed its action to pump several gallons a minute.

Structurally the human heart is a hollow muscle divided by a muscular wall, called the septum, into two pumps—the left heart and the right heart. Each of these hearts, or pumps, consists of two chambers. The upper chamber is called the *atrium* or *auricle*, and it receives the blood from the system. The lower chamber is called the ventricle and it pumps the blood out into the circulation. Between these two chambers there is a valve which permits the blood to flow only from auricle to ventricle. In the right heart this valve is known as the tricuspid. In the left heart it is known as the mitral valve. These two pumps, the left and right heart, are completely separated by the septum and their blood cannot mingle.

The heart performs its pumping action by rhythmic contraction and relaxation. The contraction is called the systole and starts at the top of the heart. It moves down like a wave, literally squeezing the blood from auricle into ventricle and from ventricle into the arteries. Then follows a wave of relaxation, called the diastole, during which the heart dilates and permits blood from the body to enter the auricles and flow past the valves into the ventricles. Then, once again, a spasmodic wave repeats the heart's pumping contraction.

The blood pumped through the heart does not nourish it. The heart is nourished via the coronary arteries, small vessels lying on its surface, and their related systems of channels.

Here we come to one of those curious mysteries that remains

despite the accumulation of considerable knowledge, superb tools, sophisticated experimental techniques and refined theory.

We do not know what makes the heart beat.

Most pumps are powered by motors. But we can detect no motor that powers the beat of the heart. Because the heart is a muscle well supplied with nerves, it was long believed that these nerves instigated the heart contraction just as nerves are responsible for the contraction of all other muscles. But while all other muscles become paralyzed when their nerves are cut, the heart muscle continues to beat. The heart has even been removed from the body, placed in a nutrient solution and there, all alone, without brain, without blood, without nerves, continued its rhythmic pulsations.

There seemed to be only one conclusion. The power that drives the heart comes from within the heart itself, from some self-contained mechanism as basic and as primitive as the very earliest life forms that possessed reflexes but had not yet developed consciousness.

Scientists investigating this curious phenomenon tried to find the location and nature of such a possible mechanism. Observations on the heart of a frog showed that the waves of contraction began near the *vena cava* toward the top of the right heart and passed down, first over auricle and then over ventricle in regular order.

By observing the embryo of the forming chick, scientists detected a bit of primitive tissue in the area around which the heart later took shape. This tissue, long before it became a heart, already flickered with a regular, even beat. In the human embryo such a primitive heart beats three weeks after gestation—two weeks before the elements of the nervous system appear.

Finally, in 1907, Sir Arthur Keith and Martin W. Flack made a discovery which seemed to lift at least part of the mystery surrounding the origin of the heartbeat. In the upper part of the right auricle, near the superior *vena cava* which carries the blood back from the head and upper part of the body, the two British physicians found a small knot of tissue extending downward about

¾ of an inch. This knot, or node, was quite different from the surrounding heart muscle. It consisted of a tangled network of primitive muscle cells and nerve fibers, with a special blood supply, embedded in connective tissue and not connected to anything but the muscle around it.

This strange tissue, named the *sino-atrial node*, undergoes rhythmic chemical changes as a result of some inner processes which we still do not comprehend. With each of these changes a wave of contraction is sent out through the surrounding heart muscle. This impulse serves as a sort of "spark" or pacemaker for the heartbeat. Each time it sends out its contractive impulse, the node discharges a measurable electrical impulse.

Whether the impulse that contracts the heart and the electrical discharge that accompanies it are actually the same thing is not known. But we do know that the impulse and the current invariably go out together, and the heart muscle contracts as the electrical current passes over it.

Apparently the sino-atrial node does not do all the work of stimulating the heartbeat. Another, similar, bit of tissue was discovered in the lower part of the right auricle, against the muscular inner wall of the septum. This was named the *atrio-ventricular node*. It sends branches of nerves radiating down into both ventricles where they form intricate networks.

This second node and its fine message network act as a relay station for the impulse originating in the sino-atrial node. As this impulse reaches the second node it is relayed through the nerve network to the muscle fibers of both ventricles, causing them to contract.

The discovery of these two nodes leaves us with a primitive heart within the heart—a sort of neuromuscular electrical generator which operates by some unknown mechanism that is independent of the rest of the body. More time, knowledge and effort will undoubtedly bring us to an understanding of the sino-atrial node and the processes whereby it generates the beat of the heart.

It is interesting to speculate on what the metaphysicians would have concluded had this mysterious bit of primitive tissue been known in earlier days. Very likely they would have seen it as the very kernel of life and, possibly, the seat of the soul.

While the sino-atrial node stimulates the actual beat of the heart at a basic rate, the rhythm is not constant. The heartbeat may slow down or speed up, depending upon emotional, physical and other factors acting upon the body. This control over the rate of the heartbeat is exercised by the autonomic, or involuntary, nervous system centered in the *medulla oblongata* at the lower part of the brain. This is the same center which, through other nerve channels, directs the flow of blood to those parts of the body that need it.

Two systems of nerves are involved in the regulation of the pulse rate. The vagus nerves tend to act as a brake upon the heart, reducing the force of the beat and preventing it from racing ahead at unnecessary speed. The accelerator nerves increase the force and rate of the heartbeat, something that may be necessary during periods of stress, excitement or heavy work.

Both sets of nerves are continuously in operation, maintaining a delicate balance of control over the action of the heart. Should the body meet a sudden stress that requires an emergency rush of blood, the accelerator nerves increase their activity, releasing a chemical similar to the hormone, adrenalin. This chemical acts as a powerful heart stimulant. When the emergency subsides and the need for blood returns to normal, then the vagus nerves increase their activity, releasing a chemical which relaxes and slows the action of the heart. This substance is known as *acetylcholine* and it resembles a drug found in poisonous mushrooms.

While the human pulse rate per minute is normally about 72, it seems to be inversely related to size throughout the animal kingdom. A human infant's heart beats twice as fast as an adult's. An elephant's heart beats about 25 times a minute while the canary's beats 1,000 or more times during the same interval.

Keeping before us this picture of the heart pump and the vessels that, together, form the cardiovascular system, let us examine the flow of the river itself as it courses through the channels of the body.

The blood, as we know, is a complex transport medium that carries oxygen, nutrients, defensive substances, hormones and other essential materials to the cells and tissues of the body, and removes such wastes as carbon dioxide, urea and other byproducts of the life processes.

The dark, venous blood returning to the heart, lacking oxygen and charged with carbon dioxide, enters the auricle at the right side of the heart through two great veins. These are the *inferior vena cava* which brings in the blood from the trunk and lower part of the body, and the *superior vena cava* which returns the blood from the head and upper part of the body.

As the heart relaxes during diastole, the blood from these veins pours into the right auricle and flows through the open tricuspid valve into the right ventricle. Then, as the sino-atrial node sends out the contracting impulse, the systolic wave forces the remaining blood out of the auricle through the valve into the ventricle. The wave of contraction continues down through the ventricle, forcing the tricuspid valve to close, the pulmonary valve to open and sending the blood through this valve into the pulmonary artery.

Branches of this artery which, with the aorta, is the largest in the body, lead the still-dark venous blood to the lungs. There it passes into a network of capillaries which surround an estimated 700 million air spaces or *alveoli* contained within the lungs. At this point, the blood discharges its carbon dioxide through the capillary walls and receives a fresh charge of oxygen. The instant this happens, the dull-red venous blood takes on the bright hue of arterial blood.

This oxygenated blood then passes from the capillaries into venules and thence into the pulmonary veins which lead it back into the heart through the left auricle.

During this passage through the pulmonary circulation which Servetus and Realdo Colombo first traced, the blood performs no positive function for the body. But by taking on its cargo of oxygen, it prepares itself for the life-sustaining work it must do in the systematic circulation on which it is now to embark.

A rather strange anomaly ought to be noted here. In all other parts of the body the arteries carry bright, oxygenated blood while the veins carry dull, carbon dioxide laden blood. This is not true for the pulmonary circulation. Instead it is the pulmonary artery that carries the dark blood to the lungs and the pulmonary veins that bring the bright, aerated blood to the heart. This undoubtedly caused great confusion among the early anatomists who sought to determine the difference between arteries and veins. As we have seen, it was a long time before we recognized arteries as those vessels which carry blood away from the heart, and veins as those vessels which carry blood on its course back to the heart.

When the heart relaxes in diastole, the oxygenated blood enters the left auricle and flows into the powerfully-muscled left ventricle. Then, as the heart contracts upon the impulse generated by the sino-atrial node, the mitral valve closes, the aortic valve opens and the blood is thrust into the great, arching aorta, the major arterial canal of the systemic circulation.

The blood enters the aorta at great pressure. This pressure sustains the blood's movement throughout the branching arterial tree and on into the capillaries. There is always pressure in the arterial system. When the heart contracts in systole, the pressure is highest. When it relaxes in diastole, the pressure decreases. These high and low points in the blood pressure can be measured, a procedure used by physicians to study the state of the heart and circulatory system.

The normal limits of blood pressure, measured on the instrument known as the *manometer*, range between 70 and 90 mm. Hg. (height in millimeters of a column of mercury) during diastole, and between 110 and 140 mm. Hg. during systole.

Many factors may make an individual's blood pressure vary during a day as well as from day to day. Excitement, fear, worry, tensions, blood loss during an accident or operation—all these may cause temporary changes of blood pressure even in people whose circulation is relatively normal.

The blood that is thrust into the aorta is modified in its spasmodic motion by the nature of the arteries. As they route the blood to the various parts of the body according to the directions carried by the vasomotor nerves, these vessels relax with each beat and contract between beats. In this way the intermittent spurt of the blood is evened out and, by the time the blood reaches the capillary bed, it is flowing in a smooth, even stream.

In the capillaries, which are so narrow that only a single red cell can pass at a time, the flow of blood is extremely slow, moving at the rate of about an inch a minute. The blood performs its ultimate function here, fulfilling the role once played by the sea. Then, dull and dark once more, the blood leaves the capillaries and enters the venules, the tiniest twigs of the venous tree.

Moving into increasingly larger branches, the blood finally enters the venous trunk—the venae cavae—and is returned to the right auricle of the heart.

During its return course through the veins, some of the blood continues to do vital work. Blood passing through the digestive tract picks up the products of digestion and carries them to the liver where they may be chemically treated, stored or routed through the blood to some other part of the body. And as blood passes through the kidneys on its return to the heart, it is filtered through intricate devices to remove urea, ammonia and other wastes.

It is impossible to comprehend the full flow of the river of life without examining one of the great engineering problems of the venous circulation—how to make the blood flow uphill.

While the arterial circulation is impelled by the motive power of the heart, the venous blood has no such pump to speed it on its way. This poses no great problem for the upper part of the body from which the blood can flow down to the heart with the help of gravity. But the blood in the lower part of the body, in the trunk and legs, must somehow make its way upward without the aid of gravity or of any special organ.

Nature, through the trial and error methods of natural selection, has solved the thorny problem in a highly ingenious way.

A number of highly effective valves are strategically placed through the veins. These valves, which had been noted by Fra Paolo Sarpi, Vesalius and others, open in only one direction—toward the heart. Blood can pass through only in that direction. If it tries to back up or move away from the heart, that motion closes the valves, preventing any backward flow. Furthermore, the veins are located between the skeletal muscles of the body. Thus, each time the body moves and one of these muscles contracts, pressure is exerted upon the veins. The blood they contain is squeezed by this pressure which forces it through the next valve closer to the heart. The valve then closes, preventing a backward flow. In this way, step by step, the blood is moved up the valvular elevator of the veins until it is returned to the heart.

If we are inactive or remain in one position too long without moving our muscles, the venous blood—especially in the lower extremities—is not given a chance to move upward and we begin to feel sluggish or uncomfortable.

In some cases, where the blood in the legs fails to return to the heart at a proper rate, varicose veins may result. This usually happens to people who must stand a great deal, whose veins lose their elasticity or whose valves fail to close properly. In any case, the blood accumulates and causes a swelling of the vein.

Apart from this defect, which is less a fault of nature's engineering than it is of human factors, the difficult problem of returning the venous blood upward to the heart is efficiently solved.

Chapter Seventeen

The Nature of the River

The blood that flows within us is much like the original sea. What differences there are arise from the fact that the sea was an external environment serving the simple cells and organisms suspended within it, and our blood is an internal environment designed to meet the more specialized demands of an organism that surrounds it.

Over its vast surface the sea came into direct contact with the air, absorbing oxygen which it could then supply to the primitive organism. The internal circulation has no such contact with the air and no similarly simple way of exchanging oxygen for carbon dioxide. To accomplish this necessary task, the blood has developed specialized structures—the red cells. In the same way, and for much the same reasons, the blood contains other elements and structures which did not exist in the original sea.

Yet, despite the millions of years that have passed since our ancestors emerged from the sea and adapted to a life on land, the fluid of our blood and the water of that early sea are almost identical in their inorganic chemical composition.

The blood that has replaced the sea then, while still basically the sea, is a much more intricate fluid in which solid elements are suspended. Just what these elements are, and what composes the fluid portion of the blood, are puzzles that have challenged scientists for hundreds of years.

Some of these puzzles have been solved and many are at least partially pieced together.

The further development of the microscope, the improvement

of microscopic techniques, the application of increasingly sophisticated chemistry and other sciences, and the introduction of newer and better tools made explorations into the nature of the blood possible.

The solid elements of the blood—the red cells, several kinds of white cells and certain structures called platelets, which are not really cells at all—are carried by the plasma.

The red cells, or *erythrocytes*, are the most numerous cells in the blood. Their function is to carry oxygen to the tissues and remove carbon dioxide. The number of red cells in the blood is subject to some variation, but the human body ordinarily contains about 35 trillion of them at any given moment. A cubic millimeter of a man's blood, about 1/25 of a drop, contains from 5 to 5½ million red cells. An equal amount of blood from a woman, for some strange reason, has about half a million fewer red cells.

Sex is not the only factor that creates variations in the number of circulating red cells. People living at extremely high altitudes, Tibetans and Andeans, may have 30 percent more erythrocytes than people living at sea level. Even people moving from low to high altitudes for a brief period undergo an almost immediate increase in their red cell count. Our red cells also increase during exercise and other muscular activity, during an emotional upsurge or when there is a rise in the surrounding temperature.

At the other extreme, people and animals that work in deep mines where there is an increase in barometric pressure have a lower red cell count than those at sea level. In every case, whenever the body needs additional oxygen, more oxygen-bearing red cells move into the circulation; whenever the body needs less oxygen, the number of red cells falls.

Two factors appear to be involved in raising the level of circulating red cells. The rate of manufacture of these blood elements may increase. Or the spleen, an organ on the upper left side of the abdomen which, among other things, acts as a reservoir for erythrocytes, may release red cells into the circulation.

The life cycle of the red cell is brief and hectic. It is manufactured by the red marrow of such bones as the spine, hips and ribs, and passes through several stages before attaining its final form. At its birth it is a relatively large cell, more or less colorless, with a sizeable nucleus and other characteristics of a living cell. As it develops it becomes smaller, gradually loses its nucleus and takes on the hemoglobin which imparts the red color. At this stage it is released into the blood to become a fully formed red cell.

The mature erythrocyte is a round, flat, flexible disc with a saucer-like depression on each side. This provides it with a greater oxygen-bearing surface and also allows it to bend and fold as it passes through capillary openings which might be too small for normal passage.

Driven around the circulation at an average speed of once or twice a minute, the red cell is subject to many strains and accidents. It is buffeted by other cells as it hastens through the vessels; it may undergo a number of other difficulties. Consequently, its life span is short, averaging between 90 and 125 days. When the worn or overage cell passes through the spleen in the normal course of the circulation, large scavenger cells called *macrophages* engulf and destroy it. The macrophages save the iron in the red cell's hemoglobin and turn this essential substance back into the body's economy.

Without hemoglobin our tissues would suffocate. This unusual substance, which gives the red cells their color, is related both to the green chlorophyll of plants and the pigments which give the feathers of birds their bright colors. But there is one important difference—hemoglobin contains iron. As a matter of fact, the blood of an average man is said to contain enough iron to make a two-inch nail. It is this iron in the hemoglobin which provides our red cells with the ability to carry the oxygen necessary to life.

As we know, when ordinary iron is exposed to air it quickly rusts as a result of its readiness to pick up oxygen. Free iron does not release oxygen readily. But the iron constitutes only a small portion of the hemoglobin. The major part consists of a pigment called porphyrin and a protein substance known as globin. And the iron, combined with these substances, acquires a unique oxygenating ability which enables it to surrender its oxygen as quickly as it acquires it. This characteristic, which we will examine in greater detail later, makes it possible for the blood to supply each cell promptly with the oxygen it needs.

Essential as they are to life, the red cells are themselves without the characteristics of life. Having lost their nucleus in the latter stage of their development, they are actually biochemical structures specially designed to do a specific job with the utmost efficiency. They have no volition, no independent movement or activity. Instead they are directed to the various parts of the body by the pressures and mechanisms that guide the flow of the blood.

In this respect the white cells, or *leukocytes,* are different. They range through the blood. Each leukocyte is a cell containing a nucleus—a characteristic of a true, living cell. What is more, they have the power of independent, amoeba-like movement which enables many of them to pass through the endothelial walls of the capillaries and move freely among the body tissues. In a large sense these are separate living entities pursuing seemingly independent existences within us. Yet they also are a part of us because their activities serve the needs of the organized system of cells to which they belong—the body itself.

The white cells contain no hemoglobin and are outnumbered by the red cells by about 600 to one—a substantial minority, for the average adult body contains about 60 billion leukocytes. These quasi-independent organisms which roam our blood and are essential to life and well being are divided into two major groups, the *granulocytes* and the *lymphocytes.* Each group, in turn, is further divided into several varieties.

The granulocytes are by far the larger group. They have a lobed nucleus and they derive their name from the fact that there are tiny granules scattered throughout the protoplasm that forms the bulk of their substance.

Since the granulocytes all look pretty much alike under the microscope, it was assumed for a time that they were alike. It took the application of a sophisticated technique to show that these cells were not all alike, that they reacted differently in the presence of certain dyes. Three distinct types of granulocytes were identified, each with different characteristics apart from their varying reaction to dyes. These are known as the *neutrophils*, the *eosinophils* and the *basophils*.

The neutrophils contain granules which stain violet in the presence of dyes that are neither acid nor alkaline but neutral. They are the body's active defenders against invasion. Serving as soldiers, policemen and clean-up squads, they attack, feed upon and engulf microbes or any particles of foreign matter they may encounter.

These white cells constitute the majority of the body's leukocytes, between 65 and 70 percent of the total. They are very much like amoeba, the single-celled animals found in ditchwater. They can move about freely in the body, projecting pseudopods and pulling themselves along by these tentacle-like extrusions. They can even leave the blood vessels and make their way to the particular body tissues that may need their help to fight off an infection or microbial invasion.

The remaining two varieties of granulocytes are the eosinophils which are stained red by acid dyes, and the basophils whose granules pick up a blue stain from alkaline dyes. These particular leukocytes are few in number, and nowhere near as motile as the neutrophils. Their purpose is not entirely clear.

Recent investigations indicate that eosinophils, the red-staining leukocytes, increase during allergic states such as asthma and when certain animal parasites such as hookworm are present in the body. This has led a few scientists to suspect that these particular white cells might have an action against parasites and allergy-producing agents. But all this is still in the realm of speculation, as yet unsupported by any body of positive evidence.

Little is known of the life cycle of the granulocytes beyond the fact that they are all formed exclusively in the red marrow. The span of the neutrophils, for instance, has been variously estimated as between several hours and 21 days. Since they constitute an active part of the body's defenses, their life expectancy is as uncertain as that of any soldier in almost constant combat. The yellowish substance we call pus, which sometimes forms at the site of infections, is the visible aftermath of such a combat. It consists of the byproducts of battle—dead neutrophils and other leukocytes, slain bacteria, fluid and the debris of shattered tissue.

The second major group of white cells circulating in the blood, the lymphocytes, are far less numerous than the granulocytes. Lymphocytes make up only about 25 percent of the total leukocyte population.

As far as has been determined, there are at least two types of cells, and possibly a third, in the lymphocyte category. The two that are definitely in this class are the small lymphocytes and the large lymphocytes. The possible member of the group is a variety of white cell known as the monocyte. None of these lymphocytes seem to act in the blood. Instead they apparently use the circulation as transportation for getting from one part of the body to another.

The small lymphocytes, only slightly larger than red cells, make up the bulk of the lymphocyte group. They have a relatively large and slightly indented nucleus surrounded by a narrow margin of protoplasm. Cells of this category are created in the lymphoid tissues rather than in the red marrow. They are found in large concentrations in the spleen and the lymph nodes—strategic glands located at important junctions of the lymphatic channels and which have an important part in the body's defenses.

As their name indicates, the large lymphocytes resemble the small lymphocytes but are considerably bigger, having about one and a half times the diameter. There are relatively few of them in adult blood but the blood of children seems to contain a considerable number. Confined largely to the lymphoid tissue, they have a large nucleus which may be oval or kidney shaped, and their outer margin of protoplasm is wider than that of the small lymphocyte. These and other characteristics have led some investigators to believe that the large lymphocyte is actually an immature form of the small lymphocyte.

The functions of the two lymphocytes are not entirely clear, although certain things are known about them and others are suspected. They do not envelop and absorb all foreign matter as do the neutrophils. Yet they do act against certain microbes. What may be more important, the lymphocytes are involved in the production of antibodies and blood globulins, substances which are basic to the body's immunity defenses against disease.

The third type of cell which is believed to be a member of the lymphocyte family is called the monocyte. It is somewhat bigger than the large lymphocyte, has a wider rim of protoplasm and its nucleus is deeply indented in a kidney shape. The monocytes move about freely and are very active in the destruction of bacteria and other invading substances. In all, the monocytes constitute about five percent of the blood's white cells.

Our knowledge of the various white cells is still somewhat primitive. We seem able to recognize and differentiate between most of them, but we have not yet been able to follow all of them through their entire life cycles. This is a severe handicap since some cells which we consider independent entities may actually be different stages in the development of the same cell. However, as our experience, knowledge, tools and techniques continue to improve, this puzzle, too, will probably be solved.

Within the blood there is still another formed element which, though neither a red cell nor a white cell, is of immeasurable importance to life. These are the small structures called platelets or thrombocytes.

The platelets are about one third the diameter of a red cell, and have a most unusual origin. They are fragments resulting from the still little understood disintegration of certain giant cells found in the bone marrow. The actual formation of these platelets was demonstrated in 1960 in a remarkable film made by Doctors Riojun Kinosita and Susumu Ohno of the Department of Experimental Pathology at the City of Hope Medical Center in Duarte, California.

By combining the microscope and a motion picture camera in an ingenious way, Drs. Kinosita and Ohno filmed the strange process of platelet formation through a tiny window that had been cut into the leg bone (tibia) of a living rabbit. Within the bone marrow, the camera fixed on certain large cells known as *megakaryocytes.* Some of these grew, matured and then divided to become duplicates of the mother cell, following the normal cellular reproductive process. But others, for reasons still unknown, followed a completely different pattern of growth.

After dividing, instead of each of these new cells developing independently, they merged again into a single cell, larger than the parent at the time of the original division. This cell grew and divided once more. Then the daughter cells, instead of remaining separate entities, merged again to become a still larger cell. This strange variation of the reproductive process continued for four generations. Then, as the daughter cells merged once more they formed an unstable giant cell so turbulent that it literally tore itself apart. Out of this self-annihilation the platelets —debris of the disintegrated giant—were born and discharged into the circulating blood.

The platelets vary considerably in size and shape and they apparently have a variety of functions in the body. By far the most important, as we shall see later, is the part they play in the formation of blood clots and the repair of damaged vessels.

The plasma consists of more than 90 percent water, constitutes about 54 percent of the total blood volume and is the main transport medium of the circulation. It carries the various blood cells as well as a great number of other substances which, unlike the formed elements, are dissolved in the fluid. Among these are nutrients, wastes and other organic and inorganic chemicals. In addition to all this there are the various substances which form the plasma itself—a still unnumbered mixture of proteins and other materials which perform a multitude of tasks and which are certainly essential to the maintenance of life. This is what comprises the remarkably uniform, slightly sticky, yellowish fluid which is the plasma after the blood cells have been removed.

After Malpighi made it clear in the 17th century that the blood was no simple fluid, investigators dedicated themselves to the arduous labor of determining its composition. The microscope could not show the substances out of which an apparently uniform entity was composed. It might reveal microbes and other otherwise invisible particles in a drop of water. But it was incapable of showing that the water was actually a chemical combination of hydrogen and oxygen. This subtler exploration demanded the sciences of chemistry and physics.

When the necessary tools and techniques were developed, experimental physiologists and other scientists showed that the plasma contained certain mineral elements and other chemicals as well as proteins. Most of these constituents were roughly identified and measured but the nature of the plasma proteins remained largely a mystery until 1941. In that year Dr. Edwin J. Cohn of Harvard successfully began his critical studies of the plasma with the aid of the efficient tool which has since become known as the Cohn Fractionator.

This device combined both chemistry and physics. The physical principle used was that of the centrifuge which, by rotating at high speed, was able to separate the solid from the fluid elements of the blood. The chemical principles were based upon subtle differences in the solubility of proteins. Thus it became possible not only to separate solids from fluids but also to begin to make more refined distinctions between various components of the plasma itself.

Today, although our knowledge is a long way from complete, we have a good working acquaintance with the major constituents of the plasma.

Plasma is a mildly alkaline fluid which provides our interior tissues with the balanced environment essential to life. This acid-alkali balance is measured by the concentration of hydrogen ions and is known as the pH. A pH of 7 is neutral. A pH higher than 7 is alkaline, lower than 7 is acid. The pH of the blood and other interior fluids of the body is about 7.43. Apart from certain secretions, only two fluids within the body are normally acid—the gastric juices which are confined to the digestive tract, and the urine which is excreted.

Contrary to certain popular beliefs, there is no such thing as "acid blood" except in extreme cases of such diseases as diabetes and nephritis when death is, at most, a few hours away. While acids and acid-producing substances, which are the waste products of metabolism, do enter the blood, they are eliminated by the kidneys and lungs. In any case they are promptly neutralized in the blood by certain chemicals such as sodium bicarbonate which help maintain the normal pH of 7.43.

The plasma itself is between 91 and 92 percent water. In this water is dissolved the 8 to 9 percent that makes up the balance of the fluid portion of the blood. Separating and identifying the various fractions that comprise the dissolved 8 to 9 percent has been and remains one of the most demanding tasks ever undertaken by man.

Almost 1 percent of the dissolved materials consist of inorganic substances such as sodium, potassium, calcium, phosphorus, iron, iodine, copper, magnesium and other elements in a number of combinations. These salts give the plasma its close resemblance to the sea out of which terrestrial life emerged.

In this saline fluid are dissolved the plasma proteins. These important constituents of the blood are taken up by the plasma in much the same way as egg white can be dissolved in mildly salty water, leaving it slightly sticky or viscid.

The proteins make up about 7 percent of the plasma and, thanks to the dedicated efforts of such men as Dr. Cohn, have been separated into five distinct major fractions.

The first is *serum albumin* which exists in the largest concentration and is important in maintaining the osmotic pressure of the plasma. This, in turn, helps keep the blood volume at the required level by regulating the exchange of water between the blood and the tissues.

Then there are three *serum globulins: alpha, beta* and *gamma.* These are associated with the body's immunity responses and the production of antibodies which help resist infection by the organisms which cause such ills as measles, mumps, influenza, diphtheria and typhoid. Certain antibodies in the beta and gamma fractions are involved in the destructive reaction against blood of an incompatible type (which may be given in a transfusion).

The fifth plasma protein is *fibrinogen.* This is the substance that is converted into the threadlike mesh of fibrin out of which blood clots are formed.

In addition to these major protein fractions, the plasma carries the products of digestion, the byproducts of metabolism and a vast number of other substances—hormones, enzymes and many additional materials that still remain to be identified. This, in the broadest terms, summarizes what we know of the composition of the plasma. Considerable as this knowledge already is, it constitutes a sparse beginning of the understanding that still remains to be achieved.

During the 20th century we became aware of the blood's division into distinct types. This awareness arose out of attempts at blood transfusion. It had been known since transfusions were first attempted that some cases succeeded while others resulted in swift death. The reason for this did not become clear until the early part of this century when Dr. Karl Landsteiner, who was awarded a Nobel Prize for his imaginative work, found the answer.

Human blood, Landsteiner discovered, was not uniform but could be divided into four main groups. These were classified as A, AB, B and O. All human races, it was shown, have the same blood groups. What differences there are exist in the percentages of each group. A higher percentage of Caucasoid peoples have group A blood. A higher percentage of Negroid peoples have group B blood. Both are about equal in groups AB and O blood.

Transfusion was disastrous when the blood of a donor was not compatible with the blood of the recipient. Antibodies in the recipient's blood agglutinated the red cells of the donor's blood, causing them to form large clumps which could not pass through the narrow capillaries. The resultant blockage of the circulation brought serious damage and even death.

Tests showed that, in most cases, people with blood of groups A and B could receive blood only from their same group or from group O. People with AB blood could receive blood from their own group and group O, and in many cases could also accept blood of groups A and B. People with group O blood, although they are known as "universal donors" since their blood is acceptable to all other groups, are not universal recipients and can receive blood only from their own group.

This preliminary understanding of the differing blood groups made possible the blood transfusions that saved so many lives during the World Wars. Later work showed that there were further differences that might make bloods within the same group incompatible.

One such factor was discovered in 1940 by Landsteiner who was then working with Dr. A. S. Weiner. After a series of experiments with the blood of rhesus monkeys, these men found another blood agglutinin which they called the Rh factor. This, it was revealed, existed in the blood of humans as well as in the rhesus monkey which gave it its name. People possessing this factor are called Rh positive, those without it are Rh negative. Caucasians are about 85 percent Rh positive. All other races are almost entirely Rh positive.

The Rh factor, it was found, sometimes was responsible for fatal transfusion accidents even where the blood was otherwise compatible. This occurred only in a few cases where the victim had received a previous transfusion or where a woman had recently delivered a stillborn child.

These clues led to the discovery that the Rh reaction takes place the second time an Rh negative is transfused with Rh positive blood. The obvious conclusion from this is that the reaction is a kind of immunity response produced only after the host has been exposed to the Rh positive blood. The Rh antibodies take about twelve days to develop. Then, when another transfusion of Rh positive blood is given, the antibodies attack the red cells of the transfused blood.

It should be repeated that this danger exists only where Rh positive blood is transfused to an Rh negative recipient. Transfusions of Rh negative blood to Rh positive hosts do not usually have damaging consequences if the bloods are otherwise compatible.

The discovery of the Rh factor explained certain birth accidents. About 13 percent of all marriages among whites in the United States are between Rh negative mothers and Rh positive fathers. Almost half of the children resulting from such marriages are Rh negative, the remainder inheriting the Rh positive factor from the father.

The first time an Rh negative mother bears an Rh positive child there is usually no apparent difficulty. But if she becomes pregnant with another Rh positive child, the consequences can be extremely serious. The mother's antibodies, developed by the first Rh positive child, may cause a condition of the fetus called *Erythroblastosis fetalis* which may result in stillbirth, death shortly after birth or, if the child survives, jaundice and anemia.

Fortunately this is very rare. Only about five percent of Rh negative mothers become sensitized by Rh positive fetuses during pregnancy, probably because the escape of blood cells from the fetus through the placenta and into the mother's circulation is an abnormal event that does not often occur.

Since the Rh discovery of Landsteiner and Weiner, a number of other blood factors have been found, and the variations seem by no means exhausted. The knowledge of these differing blood factors have proved of immeasurable value in reducing the possible dangers of blood transfusion, thus providing medicine with a life-saving tool against death from shock, blood loss and many illnesses. Recently, it has also become useful in determining questionable paternity.

Actually, blood tests cannot help solve all paternity puzzles because such tests cannot prove that any particular man *is* the father of any particular child—although this may some day become possible. They can only disprove possible paternity—and that only in limited cases.

The procedure is relatively simple. Once a blood specialist determines the blood groups of the mother and child, he can apply certain formulas of the laws of heredity to define the range of possible blood types into which the unknown father must fall. If a man's blood is not within that range he cannot possibly be the father. Should the man's blood fall within that range, he might be the father—but so could any other man of similar blood grouping. Here the blood cannot prove guilt—when paternity is considered guilt. It can only prove innocence.

All this lies within the nature of the river, the complexity of its myriad cells and the flowing intricacies of its plasma. Yet this is what man once held to be a simple red fluid, somehow synonymous with life.

Chapter Eighteen

The River Transport

The first cell could not have survived without the climate of life afforded by the sea. In the same way, each of the hundreds of trillions of cells that are organized into the human body would perish without the blood and lymph. Over the billion years and more that life has evolved, nature has developed an interior transport system that is more ingenious, more efficient and more precisely regulated than any man has yet been able to devise.

The blood actually consists of a number of transport systems. The plasma, for instance, is a vehicle for the formed elements, including the red cells, white cells and platelets, which are moved to those parts of the body that require them. The red cells in their turn serve as vehicles for the transport of oxygen to the cells and the removal of carbon dioxide.

The fluid plasma also carries in solution a host of other products as well as materials of its own substance that are essential to the life processes of the body. Apart from nutrients and wastes, it transports heat, either storing it or disposing of it in order to maintain the body within its normal temperature range. It is the medium that carries many of the body's major defenses against disease. It serves as the vehicle for hormones, enzymes and other subtle chemical and biochemical products which serve a variety of roles.

The manner in which the blood carries out a number of these transport functions is, by now, pretty well established. Other mechanisms are still in the realm of theoretical speculation and some, undoubtedly, remain to be discovered.

Since each separate cell would perish without prompt, direct delivery of essential materials and equally prompt removal of toxic wastes, the blood transport must come into immediate contact with every one of these many trillions of "clients," fulfilling the individual needs of each. The magnitude of this task is difficult to imagine, let alone fully to comprehend.

The actual pickup and delivery of this great transport organization is achieved through the microcirculation—the capillary system. These ultimate vessels permeate every tissue and are never further than five one-thousandths of an inch from any cell. So each one of the body's cells has its own individual access to the river of life.

Oxygen is probably the most immediate and constant requirement of the body. We do not have to eat continuously because most of the nutrients we need for our metabolic processes can be stored in various tissues. But this is not true of oxygen. Little of this vital material is stored and the need for it is unremitting; therefore our breathing cannot be interrupted for more than a few minutes without damage or death.

To meet this critical demand for a continuous oxygen supply, the blood has evolved a highly specialized delivery system which uses the erythrocytes, or red cells, as its vehicles. The peculiar ability of hemoglobin to absorb large amounts of oxygen and then release it instantly makes the system work. As a matter of fact, the blood's hemoglobin carries about 60 times more oxygen than could be dissolved in the blood fluids. Without this oxygen-carrying iron pigment, 300 quarts of blood fluid would be needed to supply the oxygen required by our cells.

This unique ability to absorb and carry huge quantities of oxygen from the lungs to the tissues is only one aspect of hemoglobin's contribution to the blood's transport efficiency. Hemoglobin can also move large quantities of carbon dioxide waste from the tissues back to the lungs, thus attending to both the first and last stages of oxidation.

In its oxygen-carbon dioxide exchange, the body makes ingenious use of a peculiar characteristic of fluids. Any fluid—and gases are considered fluids—will tend to move from an area of greater pressure to an area of lesser pressure. If a gas exists on two sides of a porous membrane and there is greater pressure on one side than on the other, the fluid will pass through the pores from the side with the greater pressure to the side with the lesser pressure. Similarly, a gas will dissolve in a liquid only if the pressure of that gas in the surrounding atmosphere is greater than the pressure of the gas in the liquid. If the pressure of the gas within the liquid is greater, then the gas escapes from the liquid into the atmosphere, as it does when a bottle of champagne or carbonated water is opened.

The tendency of fluids to move to areas of lesser pressure is well worth remembering since it is involved in other aspects of the blood transport as well as in a number of additional body processes.

Let us follow the oxygen transport from the moment we take a breath. The inspired air, rich in oxygen and containing little carbon dioxide, enters the lungs and reaches a system of tiny sacs which are called *alveoli*. These alveoli have extremely delicate walls consisting of some tissue fibers and a fine network of capillaries.

Within the capillaries that form the alveoli walls is the venous blood that has been sent into the lungs from the right side of the heart. This blood is dark, the hemoglobin of its red cells holding virtually no oxygen but charged instead with the carbon dioxide waste that has been brought from the tissues.

It is at this moment, when the oxygen-rich, carbon dioxide-poor air in the alveoli is adjacent to the oxygen-poor, carbon dioxide-rich blood, that a remarkable double exchange takes place. Since the pressure of carbon dioxide is greater in the blood than in the alveoli, this gaseous waste passes through the capillary walls into the air sacs of the lungs which expel it into the atmosphere during exhalation. But the pressure of oxygen in the alveoli is greater than that in the blood, so this vital gas passes swiftly through the capillary walls into the blood where it is rapidly absorbed by the hemoglobin.

Bright and rich with the oxygen that now saturates the hemoglobin of its red cells, the blood returns to the left heart to be thrust into the general circulation. When this blood reaches the capillaries, the red cells move in single file through the narrow passages. They pass alongside cells and tissue fluids that in the normal course of activity have used up their last cargo of oxygen and now hold a relatively high level of carbon dioxide. The oxygen and carbon dioxide are exchanged again, but in reverse order.

Since the oxygen pressure in these cells is lower than in the blood, the hemoglobin quickly releases its oxygen which passes through the capillary walls into the tissue fluids and thence into the cells. Simultaneously, the high-pressure carbon dioxide moves from the cells into the blood. The exchange takes places as though the oxygen and carbon dioxide passed in opposite directions through a revolving door.

At no time during this transport and exchange process does the blood ever give up all of its oxygen or all of its carbon dioxide. Even in venous blood a small amount of oxygen is retained, and carbon dioxide is never entirely absent from the oxygen-laden arterial blood.

Although carbon dioxide is a byproduct of cellular metabolism, it is itself necessary to the maintenance of life. A small portion of this gas is dissolved in the plasma, some is retained by the hemoglobin and some combines with sodium to form sodium bicarbonate.

This acid-neutralizing substance, manufactured by the body's own chemistry, circulates in the blood to help it maintain the alkaline balance necessary to life. If illness or other stress cause a rise in the body's acidity, the blood automatically increases the level of its circulating sodium bicarbonate to reestablish the proper balance.

The blood's oxygen transport system does not normally move without carrying essential cargo. Yet we must note one possible deviation which can be extremely dangerous. Easily as hemoglobin combines with oxygen, it has an even greater affinity for carbon monoxide, a gas that is absolutely useless to the life process of cells.

If there are equal amounts of oxygen and carbon monoxide in the air, the hemoglobin will pick up 250 parts of useless carbon monoxide for every part of necessary oxygen. Thus, even with relatively small amounts of carbon monoxide in the atmosphere, the cargo-carrying hemoglobin would fill most of its available space with the useless gas, depriving the body of oxygen. Then, if the supply of oxygen falls below what the cells need to survive, death results from what is commonly known as carbon monoxide poisoning.

Apart from this external hazard to which even the healthiest blood may be exposed, the hemoglobin system for the transport of oxygen seems to be the most efficient yet devised. This does not rule out possible improvements, either by continuing natural selection or by the conscious efforts of man. After all, it took nature perhaps a billion years of trial and error to evolve hemoglobin. And scientific chemistry is a scant few hundred years old.

The blood's transport of nutrients, the chemical products of digestion, is as essential as the delivery of oxygen. Without it there could be none of the metabolic processes that sustain life.

Each of the body's cells is a chemical factory requiring its supply of raw materials. Breathing provides them with oxygen. Eating provides them with basic chemicals such as amino acids, sugars, fats and fatty acids, minerals and vitamins. All these, and the oxygen with which they combine in a form of intercellular burning, are the essential substances of metabolism.

As we know, metabolism embraces two fundamental processes, anabolism and catabolism, the building up and breaking down of body materials. In the anabolic process, the simple products of digestion which the blood delivers to the cells are chemically processed and built into substances the body requires—blood, new cells, bone, muscle and other materials essential to life, health and growth.

Catabolism is the degradation of body materials. Damaged and worn cells and tissues, substances and structures that are no longer useful or necessary are reduced to simpler chemicals. They may be stored or used again in a similar or different form—just as the iron in hemoglobin is reused in the creation of new red cells—or they may be eliminated as waste.

During oxidation and the different stages of catabolism, energy is released. This energy makes possible the beating of the heart, the physical act of breathing, the chewing of food, running for a train and all of the other countless activities of the body.

As we can see from this brief description, metabolism is the biochemical activity of life itself, and the transport of the materials of this activity is the task of the blood and its associated fluids.

Before the nutrients contained in the foods we eat can pass into the body proper, they must be reduced by the digestive processes into molecules small enough to negotiate the pores of the intestinal membranes. Strange though it seems, the digestive tract is not considered a part of the body's interior. It is, in effect, a large complex of tubes and other associated mechanisms linked to and surrounded by the body. This explains why, while the body's interior must remain alkaline, powerful acids can and do function in the digestive tract. Were these acids in the body proper, they would so alter the interior environment that death might follow.

During digestion, the carbohydrates we eat are reduced to simple sugars such as glucose and the fats are reduced to glycerol and simple fatty acids. The complex proteins are reduced to their amino acid building blocks, of which some twenty-five have been identified. After the food has been converted into these small molecules, it is ready to pass into the body's interior.

Delicate, fern-like projections that are a part of the mucous membrane lining the small intestine absorb the digestive products into the blood and lymph. These tiny projections are called *villi* and they consist of a core which contain a single lymphatic vessel and a capillary loop. Each of these villi is surfaced by a single layer of mucous-secreting cells which acts as a barrier between the digestive system and the vessels within the villi. Altogether there are about five million of these villi, so closely spaced that they give the interior wall of the intestine a velvety appearance.

The process of food absorption follows the same general principles as the absorption of oxygen that takes place in the lungs. There is a higher concentration and pressure of each food substance in the intestine than there is in the blood and lymph flowing through the villi. Therefore the tiny molecules to which the food has been reduced pass through the porous barrier of the villi surfaces into the tiny vessels within.

Glucose, amino acids and some of the fats are absorbed into the capillary blood. The remainder of the fat passes into the lymph. Also absorbed through the villi into the blood are vitamins, inorganic salts and trace minerals as well as water, some of which is absorbed through the large intestine.

Once in the blood stream, the basic nutrient substances pass into the portal vein and are brought directly to the liver, the body's largest gland and its greatest chemical factory. Here the products of digestion may be processed into other substances needed by the body, stored, or sent unchanged into the blood. Some of the amino acids reaching the liver are converted into blood proteins such as albumin and fibrinogen. Other amino acids are built into protein substances required for growth or tissue repair, and still others are sent out in their simplest forms to be picked up and used as needed by the cells and tissues of the body.

A portion of the glucose that enters the liver is sent out directly into the circulation which carries it dissolved in the plasma. In that form, this sugar can be transferred to any cell or tissue that requires a source of energy. The glucose not immediately needed by the body is converted by the liver into a more complex sugar called glycogen which the liver can store until needed. If the sugar in the blood falls below the required level, the stored glycogen is converted back into glucose and discharged into the circulation. In this way, with the liver responding to signals from the blood, the body's supply of transportable sugar is kept at a relatively constant level.

Insulin makes it possible for the cells to utilize glucose and convert it into muscular or other energy. This hormone is released into the blood by cells in the pancreas. We do not know the precise action of insulin but we do know that if it is not released into the blood or if its action is somehow impeded, *diabetes mellitus* results—a disease marked by an inability of the body to utilize carbohydrates as an energy source.

About sixty percent of the digested fats are carried to the liver by the blood, the rest enter the lymphatic circulation. These fatty substances are stored as an energy reserve and used for certain critical chemical processes within the body. Some of the fatty molecules, for instance, are used in the manufacture of essential glandular secretions such as the sex hormones.

As a means of storing an energy reserve, fat is probably the most efficient substance there is. An ounce of fat can produce twice as much energy as an equal amount of carbohydrate or protein. For this reason, excess sugar and protein which is not eliminated by the body is converted into fat for storage.

The fat is normally stored in tissues known as fat depots. Whenever the body has to draw upon this reserve for energy, fat from a depot is released into the blood and carried to the liver where it is processed into energy-producing substances. These are then discharged into the blood which transports them to the cells and tissues where they will be used.

One of the major differences between animals and plants is the ability to store energy efficiently in the form of dry fat. Because dry fat is lighter and less bulky than carbohydrate (the main energy storage substance of plants), animals are better able to walk, run, crawl, swim or fly. Most plants, weighed down by a burden of stored carbohydrate are, according to this belief, rooted in one spot as much by their less portable energy reserve as by other factors. Exceptions exist, of course, most of them on a microscopic level and in the sea.

As the blood transports the nutrients to the cells it carries various chemicals as well as tiny amounts of certain metals. All these "trace elements" and inorganic chemicals are essential to the processes of life. The importance of iron has already been discussed. But without the catalytic presence of copper, the production of hemoglobin would be impeded, and without the stimulus of cobalt, the bone marrow's ability to manufacture red cells might be dangerously reduced. The thyroid gland needs iodine, bones require calcium, and phosphorus is essential to teeth and muscle activity.

The blood also carries the hormones. These potent chemical products are poured directly into the circulation by the endocrine glands which manufacture them from raw materials delivered by the blood.

Each hormone (the name is derived from a Greek verb meaning "to excite") seems to have a particular effect in regulating certain vital body functions. Some are involved in growth and normal development. Others influence our mental and physical processes, our metabolic activities, our emotions, our sexual needs and our ability to reproduce.

The endocrine glands must provide the blood with correct amounts of their hormones to be carried through the circulation to the tissues that require them. If there is a failure of hormone production, or if the blood carries too much or too little of these potent substances, abnormalities and even death may result.

Life also depends upon the blood's ability to remove the waste materials of the body's metabolic activities. Were the blood to fail in this, the body would perish from its own poisons.

As we have seen, carbon dioxide, the byproduct of oxidation, is carried to the lungs for disposal. The other waste products of the body's metabolic processes are picked up by the blood in the capillaries and conveyed to the kidneys, which serve as great filtering plants. The kidneys contain about 80 miles of tubing through which the blood passes. Every twenty-four hours they filter about 150 quarts of fluid which has been separated from the blood, removing urea and other chemical wastes. These are concentrated into about one or two quarts of urine and excreted. (A tiny amount of lactic acid waste and some urea is also eliminated through perspiration.) The purified fluid that remains, 148 to 149 quarts during a day, is returned to the blood. This process is repeated over and over with the same blood fluid. The kidneys also serve to regulate the mineral content of the blood, removing and discarding any excessive amounts.

Maintaining the body's water balance is also crucial to health and life. Even under normal circumstances, the body constantly loses water through urination, salivation, perspiration, breathing and various other ways. When the temperature and humidity are ordinarily comfortable, about one milligram of water is lost every ten minutes for every square centimeter of skin surface. In the deserts of the Arabian Peninsula or Persia, a person might lose ten quarts of water daily through perspiration. To replace this constant water loss, fluids must be taken into the body and distributed by the blood and lymph so that the necessary balance between tissue fluid and circulating fluid is maintained.

Tissues requiring water replenish their supply by drawing it from the blood through the process of osmosis. And the blood, as we have seen, normally takes water into its transport system from the digestive tract, carrying a ready supply that can be drawn upon by the body throughout the reaches of the circulation. If there is serious blood loss through illness or accident, the blood attempts to maintain its fluid level by withdrawing water from the tissues into the circulation.

The blood's function as a carrier and distributor of water is closely linked with the body's heat control system. The average temperature of the body is 98.6 degrees Fahrenheit. This is subject to some minor variations in different individuals and even in the same individual at different times of the day. For some unknown reason, the temperature in the early morning may be one to one and a half degrees lower than the temperature in late afternoon. However, the normal temperature of each person remains at a relative constant and any severe changes are a sign of danger.

Metabolic processes taking place constantly in the living cells produce heat. If this heat accumulated in the body with no means of release, the internal temperature might become too hot to support life. Fortunately, at the same time that the body generates heat, it also loses heat. Since the air around us is often cooler than the body's 98.6° F., heat passes through the skin into the surrounding atmosphere and is lost to the body. Where the atmospheric temperature is higher than that of our bodies, evaporation of our perspiration removes body heat.

In an ordinary day, an average man produces about 3,000 calories. If he lost to his environment more than 3,000 calories, his body temperature would drop; if he lost less, his temperature would rise. The heat produced must just balance the amount given off to the environment and this regulated heat transfer is mainly the task of the blood.

Just as fluids flow from the area of greater pressure to the area of lesser pressure, heat tends to flow from warmer to cooler areas. In this way, using physical processes known as radiation and convection, the body exchanges heat with the surrounding environment.

The blood absorbs and carries off heat in much the same way that the water in an automobile radiator absorbs and carries off the heat of the engine. The body performs this heat transfer by regulating the amount of blood flowing through the vessels of the skin. On a hot day these vessels dilate and more blood is brought to the surface. This blood carries heat from the body's interior and, as it passes through the skin, the heat is radiated to the somewhat cooler atmosphere.

In cool weather the vessels of the skin contract, reducing the volume of blood brought to the skin surface. This reduces the heat loss from the body's interior. This action takes place in those parts of the body that are clothed and protected from freezing.

But the vessels of the uncovered portions of the body surface, such as the face and ears, are dilated to give these exposed parts the protective warmth of additional blood.

Two other mechanisms are also used by the blood to regulate the temperature of the body and keep it within a normal range. During hot weather, the spleen contracts, releasing quantities of stored blood into the circulation. This makes it possible for greater amounts of heat to be carried to the body surface. During cold weather the spleen expands, increasing its volume of stored blood and reducing the amount of circulating blood available to transfer heat to the surface.

The radiation and convection method of heat transfer only works when the body seeks to lose heat to a cooler environment. On very hot days, when the environmental temperature is higher than the 98.6°F. of the body, this system of heat transfer would bring heat from the hotter environment into the cooler body. Under those conditions, evaporation prevents serious overheating of the body.

Perspiration and breathing cause body heat loss through the evaporation of fluids. In both these processes, the blood plays the key role of transporting the fluids to be evaporated. Blood, carrying heat from the interior, gives up some of its water to the surface tissues. This becomes the perspiration which is discharged through the pores of the skin and evaporated.

A similar phenomenon takes place in the lungs. On extremely hot days, blood passing alongside the alveoli gives up some water along with the carbon dioxide it discharges into the air sacs. This water is evaporated and exhaled, helping to remove more of the body's excess heat.

In all these ways and in many others that are not yet clear to us, the blood transport serves us. Without its efficient and regulated service, the many trillions of separate cells which make the body would falter, fail and perish.

Chapter Nineteen

The River Bulwark

The blood is man's great barrier against disease. In many ways, some so dimly seen that we can only guess at them, the blood defends us against the swarming pathogenic organisms that infest our environment.

Certain elements carried in the blood, particularly the scavenging white cells, attack invading microorganisms, attempt to localize their activity and then destroy them. But this is only one phase of the body's defenses. The blood also carries, as part of its own fluid, a wide array of biochemical substances that are involved in the destruction of infective agents, in immunity and in the other subtle processes whereby we resist disease.

The action of the white cells in attacking invading organisms was recognized in 1884 by Elie Metchnikoff, the great Russian pathologist. Metchnikoff, who made the discovery only by the chance of having survived two suicide attempts, named the voracious defenders of the body *phagocytes* after a combination of Greek words meaning "I eat cells."

He had grown up in 19th century Russia at a time when the Czar, to stifle any independent thinking that might bring revolution, placed severe restrictions on any but the "safest" activity. Even the various institutes of learning were under the grim surveillance of the secret police lest they give birth to seeds of liberal thought.

Metchnikoff was hounded to the brink of despair for his views. Unable to resist the pressures and unwilling to bend before them, he twice tried to escape through suicide and failed each time. At last he fled Russia, went to Italy and, finally, to the Pasteur Institute in Paris.

The discovery of the phagocytic action of the white cells came as Metchnikoff was watching a young starfish into whose skin he had driven a small rose thorn. He observed nothing of significance on the first day. But on the second day, as he looked through his microscope, he saw that the tip of the thorn was virtually engulfed by a swarm of white cells. Correctly assuming that the leukocytes were attempting to destroy harmful organisms brought in as a result of the thorn puncture, he formulated his theory of phagocytosis.

"An army of the small cells called phagocytes," he wrote, "which wander through the blood and tissues, were able to attack the microbes of disease and, after a struggle, they were able in many cases to kill these . . . intruders. . . ."

Today, more than seventy years after Metchnikoff's original observation, we know more about phagocytic activity. But gaps still remain in our knowledge. We have yet to clarify the manner in which the blood's phagocytes, mainly the neutrophils, are mobilized so that millions of them come rushing to an invaded area as though in response to an alarm.

When they are not called upon to deal with a specific invasion, the phagocytes wander from place to place as independent, amoeba-like organisms. Practically no part of the body is barred to them since they can pass through the capillary walls and into the tissues. Wherever they are, if they come across any organism or substance not natural to the body, they instantly attack and seek to devour it.

Microscopic studies show masses of phagocytic neutrophils blocking off an area of infection just as soldiers seal off an enemy bridgehead. These phagocytes are ravenous. Within the body of a single white cell as many as 15 or 20 microbes can be seen. These have been ingested alive and they remain alive for some time inside the phagocyte that devoured them.

In much the same way, the white cells attack and remove dead and worn out tissue, blood clots that have served their purpose and other debris that they may find in the body.

The defenses offered by the lymphocytes are even more versatile than those provided by the granular leukocytes such as the neutrophils. Lymphocytes travel through the blood but do their work mainly in the lymph nodes which act as filtering stations for the lymphatic fluid.

In these nodes the lymphocytes act as phagocytes, removing microbes, toxins and other dangerous agents from the lymph fluid. They also have another function. Somehow, although the process is still beyond our understanding, the lymphocytes seem involved in the manufacture of serum globulin, the fractions of the plasma proteins that have a critical role in the body's immunity to disease.

The cells of the reticulo-endothelial system are also phagocytic. Endothelial cells, similar to those lining the blood vessels, are found in such body structures and organs as connective tissue, the spleen, liver and bone marrow. Like the phagocytes of the blood and lymph, they act both as soldiers and as scavengers, destroying harmful organisms and removing debris.

These are the main phagocytic defenders of the body. Beyond them are the mechanisms of natural resistance and the various types of immunity.

From the moment we are born, our bodies are in almost constant contact with disease-causing organisms. We may carry in our systems the microbes of many diseases ranging from the common cold to poliomyelitis. Yet, despite our virtually uninterrupted exposure to infection, we remain uninfected most of the time. The reason for this is resistance. A number of differing mechanisms, mainly involving blood substances, enable us to keep disease organisms in check during the greater part of our lives, preventing them from multiplying into massive infections.

Resistance varies from individual to individual. Even in the same individual, the level of resistance differs from time to time. The factors that affect resistance are many and not all of them are known. They appear to include shock, physical stress, fatigue, faulty nutrition, exposure to radiation, blood loss, emotional stress and other drains on the body's resources.

While we are still hampered by our considerable ignorance of the mechanisms of resistance, we do know that this ability to hold off disease consists of many different defenses, most of which are related to the blood. For the most part, these resistance factors are either contained within the globulin fractions of the plasma or are carried by them.

Antibodies are one of the body's most effective weapons against infection. These have been known for some time, but it was not until very recently that this knowledge has begun to take on a few precise outlines.

Any disease-causing agent that enters the system and stimulates the body into a defensive reaction is known as an antigen. These include bacteria, viruses and other microorganisms, bacterial poisons and other toxins, red blood cells of an incompatible group and any foreign tissue that might be introduced by transplant or graft. The tissues of the victim, or host, respond to the presence of an antigen by producing substances specifically designed to destroy or render harmless that one particular antigen. This is known as the antigen-antibody reaction and it is involved in a wide range of immunity situations.

The manner in which antibodies work has long been under close study. Some recent theories on the subject were reported by Allan L. Grossberg and David Pressman at the National Medicinal Chemical Symposium of the American Chemical Society in June, 1960. Research by Dr. Grossberg indicated that the antibody is made up of certain amino acids arranged in such a manner that it will fit the antigen for which it is designed as a key would fit a lock, disarming it and making it inactive. In addition to the specific antigen-antibody fit, there appear to be interacting forces, apparently electrical in nature. These forces, reported Dr. Pressman, seem to bind a particular antibody to its specific antigen.

Since the antigen must appear before an antibody can be produced to combat it, immunities to certain diseases are developed only after some exposure and reaction to the agent causing that disease. But once the system has learned to make the antibody, these immunity-producing substances become readily available in the blood to prevent reinfection by the same ailment. However, antibody immunity can be stimulated only for certain ailments. For other ills the immunity may be of limited duration, its lifetime depending on the general health of the person involved, the extent of any new exposure and other factors.

If a child develops measles, his system reacts to the antigen by producing antibodies against measles. After he has recovered, these antibodies provide him with an immunity to any reinfection by this disease. But if he is then exposed to, for instance, a significant amount of radiation (the danger threshold here is not yet known), his immunity to measles and other ailments may break down.

Not only are antibodies specific and different for each disease, but there are different general types with differing kinds of action. Some antibodies fight invading microbes by blocking their activity. Others, called *cytolysins*, produce a substance which actually destroys the foreign organism. Since these cytolysins also destroy the red cells of transfused blood of a differing type, their effect is not entirely beneficent.

Another type of antibody is the *agglutinin*. These make bacteria harmless by clumping them in a mass. People infected with typhoid fever produce agglutinins in their blood which provide an immunity against reinfection. Still other antibodies, known as *precipitins*, form an insoluble compound with certain bacterial poisons and with foreign proteins, thus blocking them from further activity.

This differentiation between various kinds of antibodies is far from complete. We have managed to group the antibodies into broad categories—and this represents considerable progress—depending upon the manner in which they work. We still do not know their actual structures, the details of their creation and the specific ways in which they work.

In 1960, the same year that a new microscopic technique allowed man to view the creation of blood platelets, individual molecules of antibody were photographed for the first time. This notable achievement was made possible by the electron microscope and a special technique developed by Dr. Cecil E. Hall, Associate Professor of Biology at the Massachusetts Institute of Technology.

The photographs show the antibody molecules to be rod-like particles, visually indistinguishable from the molecules of gamma globulin, the plasma protein fraction in which they are most commonly found. These antibody molecules were found to be about 1½ ten millionths of an inch thick. Their length, for some unknown reason, varies from four to ten times their thickness.

Man's ability to remain healthy in a contaminated environment has been divided into three classifications: active immunity, passive immunity and natural immunity. In all three types of immunity, the protective substances are carried within the material of the blood proteins and actually form a part of the blood fluid itself.

Active immunity is the product of a person's own antibody response upon exposure to a particular infection. It may also be stimulated artificially by inoculating an individual with dead or weakened microbes of a disease or with their diluted toxins, as is done to prevent smallpox, rabies and poliomyelitis. Such immunity is specific to a particular disease and it is called "active" immunity because it depends upon the antibodies that are produced in the blood and tissues of the individual involved.

The body's active defenses are not called into play by the factors that produce passive immunity. Instead, antibodies created in animals or some other host that had been exposed to a particular disease are injected into an individual. A human may thus obtain a passive immunity to diphtheria by being injected with diphtheria antibodies that had been produced in a horse. Immunity against scarlet fever and measles is also passive.

Unlike active and passive immunity, natural immunity does not require some previous attack of a disease; nor does it arise from inoculations or vaccinations. As its name implies, natural immunity originates out of the body's innate ability to withstand infection. Two people, both in good health, may be equally exposed to the same disease which neither had previously contracted. One of these might become infected, the other not. A person may even withstand massive exposure to an infection and contract it at another time after a lesser exposure, for the natural immunity mechanism often varies from person to person and from time to time.

The precise causes of natural immunity are still too little known to be clearly defined. But work currently being done reveals some interesting possibilities. It had been suspected that certain blood proteins and other elements found in the plasma had some influence upon the immunity factors. In 1954 this suspicion was given powerful support with the isolation of a most unusual blood protein by Dr. Louis Pillemer of the Western Reserve University School of Medicine in Cleveland, Ohio.

This protein, which was named *properdin* (from the Latin *perdire*, to destroy), opened a new avenue to the scientific understanding of natural resistance. Early studies showed that the level of natural immunity to a great number of ailments was directly related to the level of properdin in the blood. In animals as well as in man, where the properdin level was high, resistance to infection was high. Where properdin was low, resistance declined accordingly.

Further studies showed that by itself, properdin did not appear particularly useful. But in the presence of other blood substances, enzyme-like chemicals known as *complement* and with tiny traces of magnesium which is also found in normal blood, an unusual mechanism known as the properdin system was formed. This system appeared capable of destroying or neutralizing a variety of bacteria, viruses, protozoa and other disease-causing agents.

What makes the properdin system particularly interesting is

the fact that, unlike antibodies which are specific to one particular disease, it seems to provide a general immunity to a host of diseases. Furthermore, unlike the other resistance factors, the properdin system appears to be part of an innate general immunity to non-infectious as well as infectious diseases.

In one of the more dramatic studies made in recent years, researchers at the Sloan-Kettering Institute for Cancer Research implanted cancer cells in volunteers at Ohio State Penitentiary. In some of the prisoners the cancer implants took root and had to be removed surgically. But in other prisoners the cancer cells were rejected and destroyed by an immunity mechanism of the body. Tests showed that the prisoners who accepted the cancers had low properdin levels in their blood, those who rejected the cancers had high levels.

There is not yet enough evidence to conclude that properdin rather than some other factor or combination of factors is implicated in this cancer rejection. But the possibilities are extremely interesting, as we shall see later.

More and more new protein fractions are being discovered in the plasma. To date, at least a hundred of these complex substances have been found. How many of these are involved in man's ability to resist disease is a subject for considerable research. But what we already know of the proteins and the other elements carried in the plasma shows that the bulwark of the blood provides us with a series of interlocking defenses without which we probably could not survive even the first year of life.

One of the most vital of the blood's interlocking defenses is the clotting mechanism. All of us have seen clots form when blood from a cut coagulates as it comes into contact with air. Clots, as we know, are also formed inside the body. Clotting—and it is still surrounded by some mystery—enables the circulatory system to repair itself automatically and prevent serious loss of blood from most breaks in the skin and tissues. Without this ability we would live under constant threat of fatal hemorrhage.

Until recently it was believed that the clotting process was an intermittent operation because breaks in the circulatory system were occasional phenomena. But recent observations show that the ordinary attrition of living exposes the circulatory network to constant damage. Crossing one's legs, tightening a belt, jostling in a crowd, sitting down to dinner—each of these innocuous actions may cause the rupture of some capillaries.

Dr. George Fulton of Boston University has taken rather unusual micromovies of the blood flow in living capillaries. These films show the delicate vessels rupturing under conditions that seem perfectly normal. What is even more remarkable, the films show how a clot promptly forms to plug the break.

The key to the clotting procedure seems to be the conversion of the soluble blood protein known as fibrinogen into an insoluble substance called fibrin. The fibrin forms a mass of threads that becomes the heart of the clot. This change of fibrinogen into fibrin requires a series of chemical reactions in the blood that are so involved we can barely trace their main outlines.

The substance that stimulates the conversion of fibrinogen into fibrin is an enzyme, a biochemical catalyst called thrombin. This substance is so potent that one part of it could turn about one million parts of fibrinogen into fibrin. If thrombin circulated freely in the system, its uncontrolled clotting action would soon be fatal. Fortunately, the protective devices of the body's chemistry take this into account, and the potentially lethal thrombin normally circulates in an inactive form called prothrombin. Prothrombin is changed into active thrombin only when needed, and then in the required amount.

There are also other factors in the blood designed to prevent excessive clotting. One of these is a chemical named *heparin* which is produced in the liver. Heparin helps to maintain a normal balance between the clotting and anti-clotting mechanisms of the blood.

Before a clot can be formed, inactive prothrombin must first be converted into thrombin. This is triggered by still another body chemical—an enzyme called thromboplastin. This substance which sets the clotting mechanism into motion, is only released when a tissue or blood vessel has been injured and requires the protection of a clot.

Thromboplastin is formed in two ways. When the body is damaged, the injured tissues produce a fluid which stimulates the blood into producing the enzyme. The other pathway for the production of thromboplastin is through the platelets, those small particles carried in the blood. These platelets clump around the roughened surface of a break in a blood vessel and release the thromboplastin.

Now let us follow this complicated chemical process and see how a blood clot is formed. A person bumps into a chair and ruptures some capillaries in the leg—an event of which he is entirely unaware. Platelets circulating in the blood are caught in the roughened area of the break, form a clump and then begin to disintegrate. As they break apart they release thromboplastin. This enzyme, in the presence of calcium which is in the blood, acts upon the inactive prothrombin circulating in the blood and converts it into potent thrombin. The amount of thrombin formed depends upon the quantity of thromboplastin released as a result of the original damage.

The thrombin, acting as an enzyme, sets into motion the process that changes soluble fibrinogen into the threads of insoluble fibrin which form a mat over the break in the capillary wall. This dense mesh of fibers captures blood cells and becomes the core of the clot. With this clot acting as a plug and preventing further blood loss, the body repairs the break. Then, no longer needed, the clot is dissolved and removed by various elements in the blood.

This, in relatively simple terms, describes what we know of the clotting mechanism of the blood. Many of the intermediate steps are still to be determined. We know that small amounts of a substance called antithrombin circulate in the blood to control the formation and action of thrombin, thus preventing excessive clotting. We also know that the prothrombin out of which the thrombin is formed is manufactured in the liver. Prothrombin formation, however, requires the presence of vitamin K which is produced in the intestinal tract. If there is a deficiency of this vitamin, the production of prothrombin is impeded and this, in turn, blocks the clotting mechanism.

Other elements and activities, still unknown, are no doubt involved in this important area of the blood defenses. Continuing research should bring a broader understanding of these and other problems involved in the body's defenses.

Chapter Twenty

Vagaries of the River

It is a generally accepted axiom that any increase in complexity is accompanied by a proportionate increase in susceptibility to damage or breakdown. More can go wrong with a typewriter than with a pencil. Another axiom holds that the greater the importance of any part of a machine or organism, the more critical is any damage done to that part. A cracked engine block is more damaging to an automobile than a smashed fender.

Because of the extreme complexity of the blood and its associated circulatory mechanisms, the points and areas of possible damage are very great. And, because of the blood's extreme importance to life, any damage done to it or its circulatory system can have the gravest consequences. In view of this high theoretical vulnerability, the blood's ability to maintain itself at a generally good state of efficiency and self repair is unusual to the point of incredibility.

The troubles that beset the blood can be divided into three broad but overlapping categories.

First, there are diseases of the circulatory system.

Second, there are diseases of the organs that affect the blood and circulation—the liver, spleen, kidneys, bone marrow, and so on.

Finally there are diseases that affect the blood itself—the anemias, leukemias, clotting abnormalities and ailments affecting the plasma proteins.

The circulatory system may be impaired in many ways. Cardiovascular diseases are, in fact, the greatest cause of death in

Europe and the United States. The circulating pressures may become abnormal from a variety of causes. Defects of the heart, or of the nervous or biochemical mechanisms affecting the circulation, can cause serious damage, including congestive heart failure.

Stress, infection and the ordinary attrition of living take their toll, as does a faulty diet, poor living habits, endocrine and other changes that are part of the aging process.

The valves of the heart or veins may become impaired. Arteriosclerotic changes may take place in the arteries, causing them to lose their elasticity, to harden and thicken. Fatty deposits on the arterial walls, a condition known as atherosclerosis, may impede or even block the blood flow. This could weaken the arterial wall and, if high blood pressure is present, actually produce a rupture of the vessel.

There has been an alarming increase of atherosclerosis in the United States. According to some medical opinion, it may be more a disorder of fat metabolism than an inevitable result of aging. The fatty lesions of this ailment actually begin to form in childhood and may regress or become more serious depending upon nutritional, metabolic, endocrine and other factors.

When the coronary arteries, those supplying blood to the tissues of the heart, become too narrow because of arteriosclerotic or other damage, coronary artery disease usually results. The circulation is unable to supply all the oxygenated blood needed by the heart muscle; consequently the heart is damaged. Even a moderate insufficiency of blood to the heart is enough to bring on angina pectoris with its intense pain. A serious insufficiency, such as one produced by the blockage of the blood flow by a clot or other obstruction, often referred to as a coronary occlusion or thrombosis, can be swiftly fatal.

Another serious disorder of the circulation involves abnormal resistance by the arterioles to the passage of blood. This is known as hypertensive vascular disease or, more popularly, as high blood pressure, and it affects at least five percent of the adult population in the United States.

The cause of this ailment is obscure although some malfunction of the kidneys, nervous system or the endocrines may be implicated. Heredity seems to be an important element in susceptibility. So do emotional factors, although this area is still insufficiently explored. Hypertension often damages the blood vessels, the retina of the eye, the kidneys and the brain. It may lead to such grave and frequently fatal disorders as coronary artery disease, congestive heart failure and cerebral hemorrhage.

Low blood pressure or hypotension, unlike hypertension, is rarely serious except where it results from acute blood loss, tuberculosis or as a consequence of other grave conditions.

In most cases where the blood pressure is persistently below normal but no disease is apparent, the hypotension is known as *primary* or *essential*. Beyond causing a possibly increased susceptibility to fatigue, it seems to produce no ill effects. In fact, people with primary hypotension seem to contract fewer heart and kidney ailments and may have a longer life expectancy than those whose blood pressure is higher.

The second category of troubles that afflict the blood covers those arising from diseases and malfunctions of other organs.

Ailments of the spleen and kidneys can have a direct and devastating effect upon the condition of the blood. Failure of the kidneys to remove waste materials from the blood causes a serious rise in blood toxicity and alters the acid-alkali balance.

The spleen, as we have already seen, stores blood and is associated with the destruction and removal of worn-out red cells and, possibly, white cells and platelets. It is also important in the salvage of iron from hemoglobin and, apparently, in the regulation of red cell production by the bone marrow.

Any infection or disturbance of the spleen may affect these functions, diminishing or exaggerating them and so impair the composition of the blood, causing anemia, leukopenia and other ailments. Too many of some cells may be produced. Too few or too many may be destroyed and removed from the circulation.

There may be a defect in iron salvage or some malfunction in the transfer of iron to the red marrow.

The bone marrow, directly involved in the production of red cells, leukocytes and platelets, is subject to cancer, secondary tumors and other diseases. These may change the nature of the marrow and produce serious deficiencies in blood formation.

The liver, which is the body's major chemical installation, is directly involved in the manufacture of certain plasma proteins. Liver cancer, cirrhosis and various other liver ailments impede the production of these proteins. This, in turn, leads to disturbances in the blood's acid-alkali balance, in its osmotic equilibrium, in its disease-fighting capabilities and may cause abnormalities of the clotting mechanism.

Pneumonia and tuberculosis also affect the blood. By reducing the amount of lung tissue available for the transfer of oxygen, they limit the supply carried by the red cells.

The diseases that affect the blood itself make up a third and final classification. Many of these ailments arise from causes outside the blood, making it impossible to draw any fine dividing line. We have already noted that damage to organs will produce blood changes. The same is true of nutritional, metabolic and other disturbances.

Some blood ailments seem to involve hereditary factors. Others are apparently caused by strange processes within the blood itself or by events at which we can only guess. For simplicity's sake, let us arbitrarily group them according to the blood functions or elements they affect.

Diseases that strike at the red cells or hemoglobin affect the blood's ability to carry oxygen and are called anemias.

Ailments that affect the white cells, or leukocytes, and may strike at the body's ability to resist infection include leukemia, leukopenia and might, generally, be considered leukocytic diseases.

Disorders of the globulin and other plasma proteins may reduce the number of circulating antibodies and lessen the body's ability to resist infection.

Then there are the diseases of the blood's clotting mechanisms. These cause either excessive clotting and consequent thrombosis, or result in a failure to clot and consequent hemorrhage.

Sheer prevalence makes the anemias the most important disease of the blood. Malaria and parasites—tapeworm and hookworm for example—injure the red cells, as do snake venoms and poisons such as those found in fava beans and certain mushrooms. There are many kinds of anemias, arising out of a great number of possible situations. They range from ailments so mild as to be virtually undetectable to illnesses that are inexorably deadly.

The average number of red cells in healthy blood is about 5 million per cubic millimeter for men, 4½ million for women. The blood is considered anemic when the red cell count is persistently below 4 million.

Abnormalities in the size, shape or hemoglobin content of the erythrocytes may cause anemias. Any of these defects interferes with a cell's ability to carry a full load of oxygen and increases its likelihood of destruction under the stresses of the circulation.

Anemia also results from acute loss of blood—whether from surgery, hemorrhage, or a bleeding ulcer. Since the number of circulating red cells decreases, the blood's ability to supply oxygen to the tissues is reduced. Should the blood loss be severe, it may produce the extreme physical collapse that is commonly referred to as shock.

There are several groups of blood disorders known as the hemolytic anemias. The symptoms of these ailments often resemble those of acute blood loss because the destruction of red cells is so rapid and massive that the blood literally seems to vanish.

Of these groups, the toxic hemolytic anemias are caused by different kinds of poisons. Among these are snake venom and certain vegetable poisons, as we have noted, and chemical poisons such as benzene, toluene, arsenic, and lead. Toxins produced by such bacteria as *Streptococcus viridans* and the *meningococcus* as well as by malarial and other parasites also fall in this group.

Susceptible individuals may become sensitized to certain drugs and medications—sulfonamides, sulfones and acetanilid, among others—and develop what appears to be a severe allergy reaction. In the course of this reaction antibodies are produced which destroy the red cells.

Some of the hemolytic anemias are caused by the body's formation of blood-destroying substances such as hemolysins which disintegrate the blood cells, or autoagglutinins which cause the red cells to clump or agglutinate. These anemias may result from a transfusion of incompatible blood, defects in the blood-forming system or a number of causes still unknown.

Heredity is also a factor in some forms of hemolytic anemia. One of these, called *Mediterranean Anemia* and confined mainly to people living near that historic sea, is marked by the production of unusually thin red cells. They are more fragile than normal erythrocytes and are more easily distroyed under the stress of the circulation.

Another inherited abnormality is *Sickle Cell Anemia* which seems to occur almost exclusively among Negroes. This ailment is marked by the production of sickle-shaped red cells rather than round ones. These misshapen cells, being more liable to clump in the arterioles and capillaries, are more vulnerable to damage and disintegration.

Pernicious anemia, until recently a very dangerous blood ailment, is not a hemolytic anemia. It appears to be due to the absence of an, as yet, unidentified substance in the gastric juices. This defect results in an inability to absorb vitamin B_{12} from the intestine. Since that vitamin is essential for normal bone marrow activity, blood cell formation is impaired and abnormally large red cells are formed with a life span only about half that of the normal erythrocyte.

Pernicious anemia came under a large measure of control once its cause was determined. Large doses of vitamin B_{12} usually restores normal function of the bone marrow, and this form of anemia is no longer as "pernicious" as it used to be.

A number of anemias result from hemoglobin deficiency which, in many cases, is due to inadequate iron in the diet. Pregnant women and women with excessive menstrual flow have higher iron requirements than usual and should supplement their diets to meet this need. Iron-deficiency anemias may also appear in infants kept on a milk diet for too long, or among children undergoing a period of extremely rapid growth.

A whole range of anemias arise from nutritional or metabolic disturbances and from situations involving the endocrine glands. In the majority of cases, if the anemia is given adequate attention and the underlying causes are corrected, the outlook is generally good. Yet in some forms of the disease, the prognosis is extremely poor, and most patients die in spite of repeated transfusions. Aplastic anemia and other variants of the disease that arise out of a failure of the marrow to form blood cells are often resistant to treatment and usually run their fatal course in less than six months. Fortunately, these severe anemias are quite rare and, as our knowledge of the blood continues to grow, the possibility of their control becomes more likely.

There is a particular disease of the red cells which has the opposite effect of the anemias—a sharp increase in the number of circulating erythrocytes. The major form of this ailment is *polycythemia vera* and, in addition to the rise in the number of red cells, it is marked by an increase in the viscosity and total volume of the blood. These symptoms are accompanied by enlargement of the spleen and liver, a tendency to thrombosis and hemorrhage as well as a number of other complaints involving the circulatory and nervous systems.

Like so many other blood ailments, polycythemia vera is of unknown origin. It is a disease of the middle and late years and is twice as frequent among men as women. What makes this disease particularly unusual is the fact that it is one of the few ailments in which bloodletting—that great panacea of earlier days—is of real value in treatment since it helps reduce the blood volume to normal levels.

The next group of blood ills, those affecting the white cells, often involve a reduction in their number accompanied by a weakening of the body's defenses against infection.

Agranulocytosis, in which the destruction of the disease-fighting neutrophils is the major symptom, is an important member of this group of ailments. So is *leukopenia*, an extreme reduction in the number of circulating white cells, usually as the result of a sensitivity reaction to some chemical or drug.

Exactly the reverse of these is the usually fatal disorder known as *leukemia*, characterized by an abnormal increase in the number of white cells which then crowd out the other blood elements. In every case of leukemia, the blood-forming organs are damaged, causing abnormal proliferation of cancerous white cells. In chronic leukemia, which strikes mainly in middle age, the victim may survive three to four years and, in a few cases, even longer. The acute leukemias usually run a rapidly lethal course of from a few weeks to about six months.

This cancer-like disease of the blood forming organs seems to be on the rise. Whether this is due to an absolute increase in the leukemia rate or whether it reflects more effective diagnosis and reporting is not entirely clear. If, as considerable investigation indicates, leukemia can be instigated by an excessive exposure to radiation, we might assume there is an absolute increase in the disease which may continue to grow along with the radioactive contamination of our environment. Genetic factors may be involved in susceptibility to leukemia, just as environmental factors may trigger its onset. However, leukemia's actual cause or causes are unknown. Intensive research on leukemia is under way in many centers throughout the world. Of particular interest is the work reported in 1960 by Dr. Steven O. Schwartz of the Hektoem Institute for Medical Research in Chicago. Dr. Schwartz's research strongly suggests that a virus may be responsible for at least some forms of leukemia.

Dr. Schwartz took purified, cell-free extracts from the blood of leukemia victims and injected them into mice which then developed leukemia. These same extracts produced an antibody-like response in human volunteers. Serum from these volunteers was then injected into mice which were also given doses of the original leukemia-producing extract. These antibody inoculated mice did not develop leukemia.

Equally important findings in support of the virus theory were reported in 1960 by Dr. J. B. Maloney of the National Cancer Institute. Dr. Maloney produced leukemia in mice and found that extracts from their tissues contained high concentrations of virus. This extract was then injected into newborn mice all of whom developed leukemia and died within ten weeks.

The possibility of a viral cause of leukemia is still under considerable dispute. Many physicians believe that no infectious process is involved. It might be well to note here that a similar dispute raged as recently as ten years ago when a few intrepid researchers reported that a virus might be the cause of poliomyelitis. This was sharply disputed by many medical scientists who held that no virus could possibly be implicated. Today, as a result of the recognition of the viral cause of poliomyelitis, this crippling ailment has been brought under considerable control and may even, in time, be eliminated.

Whether or not the viral theories are sustained as far as leukemia is concerned, the growing attention being focused on this disease promises to be productive. In any case, should a virus definitely be involved, neither genetic susceptibility nor environmental instigation will necessarily be ruled out since each of these may affect our tissue response to a virus as well as our general immunity to viral attack.

Leukemia is one of the blood's most dangerous diseases, but there are others, some no less lethal, that affect the nature of the white cells. These include certain types of bone tumor, cancer of the bone marrow (multiple myeloma), diseases of the lymphatic system such as lymphosarcoma and Hodgkin's disease.

Infectious mononucleosis, sometimes known as glandular fever and even as "kissing disease" also afflicts the white cells. It assails the lymph nodes and causes a rise in the number of circulating lymphocytes, many of which are abnormal. Almost any infection, even if it does not directly affect the blood will do so indirectly, stimulating the white cells into resistance. And if the infection is a severe and massive one, it may cause great havoc among the circulating leukocytes.

Diseases which affect the plasma proteins do not seem nearly as numerous as those attacking the cells and the circulatory system. This, of course, may be more apparent than real since we know much less about the plasma. One of these disorders, known as *agammaglobulinemia,* is marked by a decline or absence of the gamma globulin fraction in the blood. Since this plasma protein carries circulating antibodies and is involved in resistance, any lowering of its level is accompanied by an increased vulnerability to disease.

One form of this particular ailment seems to resemble *hemophilia* in that it is inherited and affects only male children. Other forms of the disease may result from some disorder such as nephrosis, through some defect of protein metabolism, from severe malnutrition or an extreme dietary deficiency of protein. Still another variant of this disorder may occur briefly in about the third or fourth month after birth, during the interval when an infant replaces gamma globulins transferred from the mother with those of his own.

Numerous other situations may produce a serious loss of blood proteins. Some kidney disorders cause an abnormal excretion of plasma proteins. Amoebic abscesses, cancer and other damage to the liver often impede that organ's ability to manufacture plasma proteins.

The possibilities of damage are seemingly endless if not uniformly perilous. If we consider the essential relatedness among the various organs of the body we must recognize that injury to one part will, directly or indirectly, affect every other part.

The blood ailments that affect the mechanisms of clotting,

either impeding or exaggerating them, still remain to be examined.

Those disorders that impede the blood's ability to clot are generally known as hemorrhagic diseases since they produce a tendency toward abnormal bleeding. They may arise from a number of possible causes and can make any sort of bleeding, even from a minor nick or scratch, extremely dangerous.

One such disease is caused by a fall in the number of circulating platelets, the tiny blood elements which help initiate the first step of the clotting process. If there is any defect in platelet production, or if the activity of these fragmented cells is blocked, the blood's normal clot forming procedures might not be able to start. A prothrombin deficiency, which might be caused by liver disease, a lack of vitamin K or by excessive heparin or other anti-coagulant in the circulation, produces a clotting failure.

Failure of the blood to clot may also be a byproduct of certain disorders of the plasma. A deficiency of fibrinogen, luckily a rare occurrence, would make coagulation just about impossible.

Probably the most notorious of the hemorrhagic ills is hemophilia, the "bleeding disease." Dramatized because of its prevalence among some of the more inbred royal families of Europe, this is a hereditary disorder transmitted only through the mother. With rare exceptions, however, hemophilia attacks males. The cause of this disease is unknown, but researchers suspect that it is due to the congenital absence of some normal but still unidentified plasma protein that is essential to the clotting process.

Hemorrhagic disturbances may also arise from abnormal fragility of the capillaries which, rupturing easily, send their blood oozing into the spaces around the vessels and through the skin. One form of such capillary fragility is due to a vitamin C deficiency. Another form, *purpura simplex*, is found in a number of individuals, especially women, who tend to bruise easily and without apparent cause.

Most hemorrhagic diseases have so-called natural causes, but there is at least one that is man-made. This is the clotting failure induced by anti-coagulants such as heparin. These drugs are part of the modern treatment for cardiovascular disease, used to remove clots or prevent dangerous clotting. These drugs make the possibility of excessive bleeding from any wound a serious problem. When former President Dwight D. Eisenhower, who had been receiving anti-coagulent therapy following his heart attack, required surgery for ileitis, it was necessary to restore the blood-clotting mechanism before the operation could be attempted.

The opposite of the hemorrhagic diseases—and just as dangerous—are those that produce excessive clotting. There are many reasons, and not all of them entirely clear, why the blood may develop either an inability to dissolve clots or an excessive tendency to form clots. There might be a deficiency of anti-prothrombin, heparin or some other anticlotting factor normally circulating in the blood. Excessive clotting might be produced by arteriosclerosis and, as some scientists suspect, by abnormally high fat levels in the blood. In addition, dietary, metabolic and emotional factors might also affect the clotting process.

A clot, or thrombus, lodged in a blood vessel will impede or even stop the passage of blood. Should this take place in the brain's circulation, the result is stroke or apoplexy. Coronary thrombosis, a clot blocking the blood supply to the heart, is one of the main causes of sudden death from heart attack. Pulmonary thrombosis, a clot blocking the pulmonary artery, also is swiftly fatal.

Not all thrombi, fortunately, are fatal. A clot in a vein may produce an extremely painful inflammatory ailment called thrombophlebitis. Such clots, however, must be removed or dissolved as quickly as possible lest they cause irreversible damage.

In some cases, surgical removal of a clot is deemed essential. Most often, where excessive clotting does not produce sudden death, it can be brought under a measure of control by the administration of heparin, coumarin derivatives or other anti-coagulents. This relatively recent form of therapy marks a notable advance in the science of healing. Yet, it falls far short of the corrective balance possessed by normal blood in which the clotting and anticlotting factors keep each other under effective, automatically regulated control. Man still has a long way to go before he can match nature's mechanism.

We have not, of course, covered all the diseases of the blood. But in this grim catalogue of potential pain and disaster, the blood's ability to cope with most of its problems stands out. It is this ability which has enabled us to survive.

Chapter Twenty-one

The Shadowed Zone

The earliest signs of man's appearance on earth an estimated million or so years ago are some crudely chipped pieces of stone. Yet, even before he learned to shape these rough tools man probably knew something about the blood and, through some magical process, related it to life.

At the very most, the three hundred years since Malpighi completed the map of the circulation with his discovery of the capillaries represent a flickering instant of the age of man. Yet, in that fragment of time we have gathered the bulk of our present knowledge of the blood.

A study of the blood's cellular components had to await the improvement of the microscope and the development of adequate microscopic techniques. Our understanding of the composition of the blood fluid is even more recent and could not have been attained without modern biochemistry and such advanced tools as the electron microscope, radioactive tracers and the Cohn Fractionator.

In this period of intensive research, some newly elucidated fact or observation may change the substance of some earlier conclusion, some new tool or improved technique may open some unexpected pathway to be explored. What should concern us now is the shadowed zone—the area just ahead which, while not yet fully revealed to our advancing knowledge, is no longer hidden by impenetrable ignorance.

We have a rather good picture of the physical pathways of the circulation. The revolutionary knowledge that Servetus, Sarpi, Cesalpino, Harvey and the other explorers risked so much to attain is today common information. We have a fairly useful understanding of the total mechanics of the circulation, why and how the blood moves as it does. But here the light is tinged with shadow. We still do not know all of the biochemical, nervous and bioelectrical mechanisms that stimulate the heartbeat and regulate the directions of the blood flow.

We have some knowledge, many theories and more speculations regarding the factors that may influence the blood pressure.

We do not know with anything approaching scientific clarity the manner in which many of the blood cells are formed. We have recently watched the formation of platelets and certain other blood elements, but we are unable to trace the step-by-step process that instigates the formation of these cells and carries it through to completion. If we discovered these details of platelet formation, we might find it possible to correct the defect of blood clotting that results from a low level of these cells in the circulation.

Recently some surprising clues indicated that a number of the leukocytes in the blood do not seem to have any particular function. Instead, they seem to wander through the circulation, ready at any moment to be transformed into whatever specific white cells the body might need for an emergency. They can become phagocytes or fibroblasts—cells used in the construction of bone, muscle and other solid structures of the body. They can even be converted into fatty cells.

This strange characteristic of young, mononuclear cells was discovered in the spring of 1960 by Dr. Nicholas L. Petrakis and a group of investigators at the University of California Medical Center. Typically, this finding evokes more questions than it answers. How are these cells changed? What determines the type of cell they are to become? What mechanisms govern these events?

If we could answer these questions we might be able to intervene in these processes. We might even be able to support the body and help it create cells it needs in time of stress. Perhaps we could stimulate fibroblast creation to speed certain types of healing and bone repair, or stimulate the formation of phagocytes to help ward off infection.

Deep shadows lie over our knowledge of the fluid constituents of the blood. At least one hundred different types of plasma proteins have already been identified. But protein is one of the most complex substances we know and it is capable of an almost infinite number of variations. Many of the differences are so slight that we still do not have the means of clearly distinguishing one minor variant from another. What we might identify as a single protein might actually be a number of variations so close in appearance that we cannot tell them apart—and each variation might have a different effect upon the body.

We have already noted how antibody molecules were recently seen for the first time under an electron microscope and found to resemble molecules of gamma globulin, the blood protein that carries them. This raises a whole series of questions. To pose just one: Is it possible that antibody molecules and gamma globulin molecules are interchangeable forms of the same substance?

Evidence reported by Dr. Florence R. Sabin, the noted American hemotologist, indicates that the antibodies found in globulin consists of the same protein as the globulin itself, and that the mechanism that creates the antibodies is virtually the same as the one which synthesizes normal serum globulin. This is evidence, of course, not proof. Perhaps more discriminating tools and techniques will show clear differences in these and other protein molecules that now seem to be identical.

Recently discovered immunity factors such as properdin and complement—scientists are by no means agreed on this—may be as important as the antibodies in man's resistance to disease. Just how these substances are produced and how they come together to form an immunity system still largely remains to be determined. But current research holds out hope of at least a partial answer in the near future.

Work with these still mysterious substances has already yielded important new knowledge—that the blood may have built-in defenses against non-infectious diseases such as cancer. It remains to be seen whether continuing investigation will support this initial evidence. Properdin may be only a part of a larger non-specific defensive network. Even so, with the knowledge presently available, hopes are rising that some means may be found to enhance these non-specific defenses just as ways have been found to provide specific antibody immunities by vaccination and inoculation.

Work along these lines is being conducted in a number of research centers. Initial results support the hope that the body's natural immunity defenses can be bolstered and strengthened.

One aspect of this was borne out in Progress Report XI, issued in June, 1958, by the Sloan-Kettering Institute for Cancer Research: "There is reason now to believe that natural defenses against cancer exist. . . . It has proved possible, by manipulating and enhancing these defenses, to cure in laboratory animals, some types of transplanted cancer. . . . In controlled experiments, it has been possible to immunize human beings against transplanted cancers, although not against their own."

Properdin has already been isolated from the blood with the Cohn Fractionator. Scientists are investigating its chemical structure and the manner in which it is produced in the system. Should this work prove successful, it might eventually lead to the synthesis of this complex substance.

Meanwhile, although only small amounts are available, properdin is being used in an experimental effort to boost the defenses of some grievously ill patients. Many more trials and considerable time will be required before any reasonably accurate evaluations can be made from this work.

Still another approach to the possibility of enhancing natural resistance emerged from the discovery that the injection of certain substances stimulate the body to produce a high blood-level of properdin. One of these substances is a yeast derivative called *zymosan*. Another is a material obtained from the cell walls of bacteria. This is known as a bacterial lipopolysaccharide—a complicated substance built up of molecules of fat and sugars.

Sloan-Kettering scientists implanted mice with a highly malignant cancer that is usually 95 percent fatal within three weeks. Some of these mice received zymosan to stimulate their properdin defenses. The cancer ran its normally fatal course in the control group. But in the properdin-stimulated mice, according to the Sloan-Kettering report: ". . . the cancers were gradually dissolved until they disappeared entirely. The animals were then completely cured. No cancer has ever returned, and strong immunity to a second implantation has been demonstrated as long as eleven months after the first growth was initiated."

We know that radiation, even in small doses that are otherwise considered harmless, depresses the immunity system of the body and causes a drop in the properdin level, making an individual more susceptible to infection. Intense exposure causes even the normally peaceful microorganisms in the gastrointestinal tract to flare up. This disorder is a part of the modern ailment known as "radiation illness." Recent investigation indicates that the properdin levels of the blood may be intimately involved in radiation effects.

A number of mice were exposed to intensive radiation. Some of these mice were then given booster additions of properdin. The control animals died quickly of radiation illness. The properdin-supported mice were able to survive.

It must be emphasized that properdin remains a matter of considerable controversy, and scientists are not at all agreed on its role. It may be, as some researchers suggest, that properdin is actually some other substance or combination of substances, and that the so-called properdin-complement effect might be the result of some other mechanism, still unrecognized.

By a peculiar quirk of human progress, immunity has, in one situation at least, become a serious disadvantage. Had surgery and its associated sciences not advanced to the present high level that makes the transplantation of organs possible, the sting of this irony would never have been felt. But the substitution of healthy organs for damaged or diseased ones has become feasible. There is only one crucial obstacle—immunity. Thus, while it protects man from disease, immunity also blocks one of the greatest potential advances in the preservation of life and health. But here too, research may soon produce a solution.

We know that the blood's antibodies and other immunity factors will attack any foreign protein introduced into the system. If skin or any organ that requires a supply of blood is grafted or implanted from one person to another, the immunity mechanisms of the host's blood destroy it in about ten days. A second such graft or implant is destroyed in about three to four days. This is why skin for grafting is taken from another part of the body of the person requiring the graft. His antibodies will not attack his own skin as they would another's. Hence transfers of skin or organs are only possible between identical twins, because the body chemistry of such twins is identical and the immune mechanisms do not go into action.

Today, since the transplanting of skin, liver, kidneys, adrenals and other organs is surgically possible, the protective action of the blood is sometimes considered one of nature's enormous blunders. Of course, nature had no way of anticipating this particular development of human skill.

Scientists have attempted to bypass the barrier of immunity, or at least depress it temporarily so that an implant or graft could be accepted by the host. In 1960, a major success was announced that may lead to an ultimate solution of the problem of organ transplants.

In 1958 John Riteris, a young man in his early twenties, had been found to be suffering from simultaneous failure of both kidneys. Ordinarily, this should have been rapidly fatal. He had a twin, Andrew, but he was a fraternal and not an identical twin. This ruled out the possibility of a transplant that would not be destroyed by John's own immunity reaction.

With John's death apparently inevitable, a brilliant team of doctors from Boston's Peter Bent Brigham Hospital and Harvard

Medical School made a historic decision. Headed by internist John P. Merrill who coordinated their work, they decided to go ahead with the transplant and try to save it from destruction in John's body by depressing the young man's immunity mechanism with massive doses of radiation.

The patient was subjected to a hazardous whole-body exposure to X-rays that could easily have been lethal if less carefully controlled. Then, with the body defenses virtually wiped out, the kidney was transplanted from Andrew to John, leaving each twin with a single kidney.

During this period, and until John's antibody defenses could be restored to normal, he was treated first against radiation sickness and then against the possibility of other infections to which his lowered resistance left him prone.

About eight months after the transplant, John's restored immunity factors began to attack the kidney. There was only one way to save him—another massive dose of whole-body irradiation. In some manner that is not yet understood, this second irradiation appeared to alter the relationship between the grafted kidney and John's immunity responses. The kidney has since come under no further antibody attack and has apparently been accepted. Only time will tell if the radiation exposure will produce other effects.

In addition to Dr. Merrill, the team that performed this momentous operation consisted of surgeon Joseph E. Murray, radiologist James B. Dealy, urologist J. Hartwell Harrison and pathologist Gustave J. Dammin. A similar operational success has since been reported from France but a number of other attempts have failed. Obviously, much still remains to be learned, particularly about the narrow range of radiation dosages which is so critical that it allows virtually no margin of safety. But the outlook holds enormous promise. We are drawing close to the fulfillment of the age-old surgical dream—the replacement of damaged or overage organs.

The role of the blood in such vital processes as metabolism is another area that awaits further study. In the disease known as *diabetes mellitus* there is an inability to metabolize carbohydrate, usually as a result of the absence or functional failure of insulin, the pancreatic hormone.

A number of possible causes of insulin failure have already been indicated. One of these is a defect in the blood's ability to stimulate the pancreas into secreting the hormone. This is normally achieved by a rise in the glucose level of the blood entering the pancreas.

Another suspected cause of insulin failure was reported by Dr. I. A. Mirsky, a noted American investigator, who showed that an enzyme called insulinase could inactivate the pancreatic hormone. The abnormal presence of this enzyme, found in the blood, liver and other tissues, could well be a factor in the onset of diabetes.

So, just as infective diseases might arise from a failure of the blood's protective mechanisms, some metabolic and other non-infective diseases might arise from a defect or abnormality involving the blood. Here is a vast area to be explored, and a few tentative but promising steps have already been taken.

It has long been suspected that some mysterious factor in the blood is related to that crippling disease, rheumatoid arthritis. This suspicion was confirmed in 1959 when scientists in Sweden and the United States isolated a protein substance which exists in the blood of rheumatoid arthritics but not in normal blood. This substance has come to be known as the "rheumatoid factor."

A group of investigators at the New York Hospital of Special Surgery has found that the rheumatoid factor behaves like an antibody in many respects, and is produced by cells that are known to produce antibodies. This means that an abnormal antibody response may be involved in rheumatoid arthritis.

In any case, the isolation of the rheumatoid factor makes it possible, by means of a blood test, to detect this disease in its very early stages. And, of course, it can be treated before serious damage has been done. Whether or not this strange protein fraction is a cause of arthritis or one of its consequences is still to be determined. Whatever it is, its discovery should lead to a further understanding of the arthritis-producing mechanism, and possibly to the prevention of this painful chronic ailment.

The discovery of the rheumatoid factor represents only a small portion of the intensive research currently being conducted to determine what specific blood changes can be related to specific diseases.

At the Johns Hopkins School of Public Health, investigations reported by Dr. Winston H. Price indicate that blood tests may be able to detect the presence of many serious ailments in their incipient stages. Should further experiments bear this out, medicine may reach one of its great goals—a universal diagnostic test of the blood to detect the presence of disease in its earliest and, often, most curable stage.

There is substantial evidence that virtually every disease causes specific changes in the blood. Where these changes can be identified and charted, the presence of the disease can be detected. Experiments have already shown that even mental illness such as schizophrenia produces its own characteristic patterns in the blood serum.

In a sense, these characteristic blood changes might be considered "biological fingerprints" of disease. They appear to take place in a blood fraction known as the serum mucoids, a recently-discovered group of substances consisting of specific proteins combined with any one of a large number of sugar molecules.

Dr. Price and his associates have found that the structural pattern of these mucoids seems to change with each abnormal condition. Each one of these changes, it further appears, is characteristic for each disease. Specific patterns have already been detected for rheumatic fever, kidney diseases such as nephritis and nephrosis, tuberculosis, various heart ailments, three types of mental disease, and cancers of the kidney, prostate, lungs and gastrointestinal tract.

It is worth noting that these investigations began in the spring of 1955 as a systematic study of the blood fractions of children suffering from rheumatic fever. When the tests showed that the serum mucoids were highly sensitive indicators of the disease —in its incipient as well as its overt state—the studies were extended to other ailments. Although the work is far from complete, the results show promise.

Other investigations into the nature of the blood may soon bring us close to yet another triumph—the possibility of detecting in advance the threat of arteriosclerosis and various other heart and circulatory ailments. Studies are under way to learn whether there is a measurable relationship between the fat levels of the blood and the onset of cardiovascular damage. Scientists engaged in this research hope that, by determining such a relationship if it exists, they will be able to devise a blood test capable of detecting, in advance, the likelihood of circulatory damage. This would clear the way for prophylactic measures to prevent anticipated heart attacks, circulatory disorders and even strokes.

Still other shadowed areas of the blood are yielding to the light of man's understanding. We now recognize at least 42 different mechanisms that can produce a rise in blood pressure. Further clarification of these processes should make it possible to make clear distinctions between the various types of hypertension and to develop specific treatments for each of them. Meanwhile, certain chemical agents may soon facilitate a sharp reduction or even elimination of many cases of high blood pressure.

Chemical agents are also helping provide an intermediate solution for many defects of the blood clotting mechanisms which lead to excessive bleeding on the one hand and abnormal clotting on the other. The anticlotting agents will provide an expanding margin of protection against thrombosis, embolism and stroke until a more fundamental solution is found.

Other blood ailments such as the many kinds of anemia are coming under broader control. Even deadly leukemia, in a few experimental cases, is being treated with the transplantation of healthy, blood-forming bone marrow following an immunity-lowering whole-body irradiation to make the transplant possible. More work and time are necessary before the results can be assessed, but the prospects here, too, are encouraging.

The work of today's scientific pioneers is both too broad in scope and too varied in detail to permit more than a generalized sweep of the research trends. But all the roads lead to a common meeting place—the improvement and extension of life.

Man's enduring struggle against disease is, at its root, a continuous rebellion against enfeeblement and death. Each morsel of new knowledge we gain of the blood adds another weapon to the arsenal of that rebellion.

Death, to repeat the old truism, is an inevitable consequence of life. Some scientists have suggested that the body actually begins to die at puberty, as soon as it can fulfill its biological purpose of reproduction. The process of natural dying, however, is slow and subtle. By making this process even slower and subtler, we both increase the life span and lengthen the period of vigorous, productive living. The accumulated stress and damage wrought by even the usual illnesses of a lifetime affect the quality and duration of life. If we can improve our ability to withstand these illnesses or, better yet, avoid them by improving our resistance, we will inevitably reduce the attrition that hastens decay and death.

There is a very close relationship between resistance and death according to Dr. Harry S. Simms, who conducted a series of studies at the College of Physicians and Surgeons, Columbia University, New York.

"Ninety percent of the deaths in the United States each year," declared Dr. Simms in a summation of his findings, "result principally from the progressive loss of resistance to disease with advancing years."

Some of the most provocative research into the prolongation of life was conducted by Dr. Alexis Carrel several decades ago.

He extracted a fraction from the blood of old roosters which he then added to a culture of live tissue. The tissue cells stopped proliferating, aged rapidly and died.

Carrel speculated that the blood of these old roosters must contain some aging or "death factor," an accumulation of toxins that increases with the passage of time, lowers the efficiency of the life processes and helps bring on the symptoms of aging.

This suggested another experiment to Dr. Carrel. He took an eighteen-year-old dog so enfeebled by age that he scarcely had the vitality to feed himself, and withdrew about two-thirds of the animal's blood in two separate operations. The blood cells were washed in sterile Ringer's solution, which closely resembles the blood fluid as far as the major inorganic salts are concerned. This blood, presumably cleared of the "death factor," was then returned to the dog.

The results were amazing. The animal suddenly became energetic. His dim eyesight sharpened, he started to grow a new coat, he barked, jumped, ran and even developed renewed sexual interest. Sadly, the rejuvenation did not last. After a short period of restored youth he aged rapidly, possibly because his tissues produced a mounting level of the "death factor." His sight failed, he began to lose his new coat and, once more, he became apathetic.

This experiment, reported in the book *Biological Time* by Pierre Lecomte du Noüy, who was Carrel's associate at the Rockefeller Institute, opened a great area of speculative possibilities which still remains to be explored.

While Carrel's "death factor" was never precisely identified, the discovery of another possible aging factor was announced in 1960 by Dr. Bernard Strehler of the National Heart Institute. Dr. Strehler, directing a group of investigators at the Baltimore City Hospital, found that as we get older, tiny, golden-brown granules steadily accumulate in the human heart. These granules are a type of organic pigment known as lipofuscin, which is made up of certain fatty molecules and phosphorus. They accumulate in the heart at a constant rate from childhood to death regardless of sex, race or the condition of the heart itself, and they seem to have a fundamental part in the aging process.

The "aging" granules were found in all except the very young. As they accumulate through the years, they may occupy as much as ten percent of the space within the heart muscle and actually constitute about thirty percent of its total solids. Dr. Strehler concluded that the presence of the granules in such quantity progressively impedes the action of the heart.

"Replacement of one third of the functional mass of a muscle with a noncontractile agent could certainly result in change and probable impairment of cardiac performance."

Just how these granules are formed remains to be determined, although there is some evidence that similar granular pigments accumulate in nerve ends when the diet is deficient in vitamin E. Nor do we know whether this substance is in any way related to Carrel's "death factor," the nature of the process of which it may be a part and whether it is a factor that we can learn to influence, thus retarding still further the inexorable advance of aging and death.

These and many other questions remain to challenge man as he advances toward greater knowledge. The answers he finds will reveal newer questions, spurring him to draw ever finer distinctions between what he knows and what he does not know.

Here we may have a measure of man's growing wisdom. As long as he can say: "This I believe I know but will continue to test; that, I do not know and will therefore seek to learn," man will have an effective guide in his striving toward an understanding of himself and his environment.

Selected Bibliography

Ashley-Montagu, M. F. *Introduction to Physical Anthropology.* Thomas, Springfield, 1945

Atkinson, D. T. *Magic, Myth and Medicine.* World, New York, 1956

Bernal, J. D. *Science in History.* Cameron Assoc., New York, 1957

Best, C. H. and Taylor, N. B. *Physiological Basis of Medical Practice.* Williams & Wilkins, Baltimore, 1950

——— *The Human Body.* Holt, New York, 1956

Bettelheim, Bruno *Symbolic Wounds.* Free Press, Glencoe, Ill., 1954

Breasted, J. H. *The Edwin Smith Surgical Papyrus.* Univ. of Chicago Press, Chicago, 1930

Brim, C. J. *Medicine in the Bible.* Froben, New York, 1936

Camac, C. N. B. *From Imhotep to Harvey.* Hoeber, New York, 1931

Castiglione, A. (edit. by E. B. Krumbhaar). *A History of Medicine.* Knopf, New York, 1958

——— *The Renaissance of Medicine in Italy.* Johns Hopkins Press, Baltimore, 1934

Ciba symposia. *The Circulation of the Blood.* Vol. 1, No. 3, June 1939

——— *Medicine in Ancient Egypt.* Vol. 1, No. 10, Jan. 1940

Dampier, W. C. *A History of Science.* Cambridge Univ. Press, Cambridge, 1944

Dawson, W. R. *The Beginnings—Egypt and Assyria.* Hoeber, New York, 1930

Ebbell, B. (trans.). *The Papyrus Ebers.* Milford, London, 1937

Frazer, J. G. *The Golden Bough.* Macmillan, London, 1910. Third ed. rev., 13 vols., St. Martins, New York, 1955

Freud, Sigmund (edit. by A. A. Brill). *The Basic Writings of Sigmund Freud.* Random House, New York, 1938

Gordon, B. L. *The Romance of Medicine.* Davis, Philadelphia, 1944

Hemmeter, J. C. *The History of the Circulation of the Blood.* Johns Hopkins Univ. Hosp. Bulletin, Vol. XVI, No. 170, May 1905

Henderson, L. J. *Blood.* Yale Univ. Press, New Haven, 1928

Houssay, B., et al. *Human Physiology.* McGraw-Hill, New York, 1955

Jayne, W. A. *Healing Gods of Ancient Civilization.* Yale Univ. Press, New Haven, 1925

Leake, C. D. *Old Egyptian Medical Papyrii.* Univ. of Kansas Press, Lawrence, Kansas, 1952

Lecomte de Noüy, P. *Biological Time.* Methuen, London, 1936

Lubbock, J. *The Origin of Civilization and the Primitive Condition of Man.* Longmans, London, 1911

Morse, W. R. *Chinese Medicine.* Hoeber, New York, 1934

Moulton, F. R. (ed.). *Blood, Heart and Circulation.* Amer. Assn. for The Advancement of Science, Lancaster, Pa., 1940

Patten, B. M. *Human Embryology.* Blakiston, New York, 1953

Payne, J. F. *English Medicine in the Anglo-Saxon Times.* Clarendon, Oxford, 1904

Peacock, E. *Superstitions Concerning Human Blood.* Antiquary, n.s.v. 38, London, 1902

Pillemer, L. *The Properdin System.* Trans. N.Y. Acad. of Sciences, 17:526, May 1955

Riesman, D. *The Story of Medicine in the Middle Ages.* Hoeber, New York, 1935

Sigerist, H. E. *The Great Doctors.* Norton, New York, 1938

Simpson, M. W. H. *Arab Medicine and Surgery.* Oxford Univ. Press, London, 1922

Singer, C. J. *Greek Biology and Greek Medicine.* Oxford Univ. Press, London, 1922

Sloan-Kettering Institute for Cancer Research. *Progress Report XI.* New York, June 1958

Sprat, T. *The History of the Royal Society of London.* London, 1667

Thorndike, L. *A History of Magic and Experimental Science.* Macmillan, New York, 1941

Walsh, J. J. *Medieval Medicine.* Macmillan, New York, 1920

Index